MEDICAL
GRAPHOLOGY

MEDICAL GRAPHOLOGY

MARGUERITE DE SURANY

Translated from the French by
C. C. Elian

SAMUEL WEISER, INC.
York Beach, Maine

First published in 1991 by
Samuel Weiser, Inc.
Box 612
York Beach, Maine 03910

Library of Congress Cataloging in Publication Data

de Surany, Marguerite.
    [Essai de graphologie médicale. English]
    Medical graphology / Marguerite de Surany.
        p. cm.
    Translation of: Essai de graphologie médicale.
    1. Graphology. 2. Diagnosis. 3. Medicine, Chinese. 4.
    Yin-yang.
I. Title.
RC71.3.S8713   1991
616.07′54 – dc20   90-12800
                                                            CIP

ISBN 0-87728-703-1
BJ

Translated by C. C. Elian, with special thanks to J. M.
Clarke.

Tarot illustrations are from the Oswald Wirth tarot deck
published by U. S. Games, Stamford, CT. Used by
permission.

Typeset in 11 pt. Times
Printed in the United States of America

Table of Contents

Translator's Note

Since this book on graphology was translated from the French language, the question arose: what differences, if any, are there between French and American handwritings? At one time there was, indeed, a pervasive look to French handwriting because the so-called standard model was rigidly interwoven into the educational system. And yet it has little hold today. Throughout the century, along with other European countries, to one degree or another, France has seen the increased conceptual liberation of the individual and the self-expression that is then bound to follow.

Though elderly people might be trained in the standard model (see page 166) this still does not exempt them from graphological analysis. The same factors of letterform evaluation, such as large or small, thick or thin, open or closed, consistent or inconsistent, angular or round, and so on, still apply. People will always express in detail, the conditions of a personal world in their handwriting — regardless of the conditioning effects of an educational system.

The reader already familiar with graphological practices will be introduced in *Medical Graphology* to the addition of another dimension of information that can be derived from an analysis: namely that of the physical/organic state of the writer.

There is a marked advantage in this, for to perceive the physical condition is to be guided toward direct action that is remedial in its purpose. To know only the psychology of a person is foremostly to have information without necessarily a call to curative action. Though a person may have a difficult character, unless he or she behaves with obvious irrationality and even though he or she may have an underlying organic cause for the character imbalance, nothing is likely to be done about it. But an unhealthy organ or physical condition, from the initial stage on, is unambiguous in its needs: it needs to be healed.

Along with the physical aspect and in yet another direction from that of traditional graphology, this book will also incorporate a holistic perspective.

As for the reader new to the field, the beginner may as well begin here. Graphology is not mastered in the reading of any one book. It is a constant build-up of sensitivity to detail, along with cultivating understanding of the nature of form. With *Medical Graphology* as a starting point, the new student can learn to consider and analyze in terms that are all-encompassing and encourage transcendence of finite views. The new student will learn terms, such as yin/yang, enlightenment, macroscosmic/microcosmic, patterns of balance, and other concepts that are guided by the acknowledgment of the interplay of all forms of life and the equal value of all beings; this will help develop a feeling for the letters and what they symbolize.

From the first multi-directional steps, the student can absorb the holistic principle that the various shadings of matter and spirit affect and reflect each other. Every outward movement leads to a complementary inward motion so that to undertake a holistic journey is to nurture the development of a holistic self.

Because it is a powerful tool, it is essential for the beginner to keep in mind at least these two guidelines: 1) know the conditions, as much as possible, under which a sample was written; writing surface, circumstances, even writing implement, it all needs to be taken into account. And 2) it is meaningless and misleading to come to an evaluation on the basis of a single letter. Of course all letters need to be perceived on their own, but ultimately, only in relation to one another. A hasty scan is not in the spirit of graphology; to identify forms clearly and perceive the interaction of their natures, is.

Many reasons and feelings inspired the self-initiated translation of this book. They range from the predominantly functional to the predominantly aesthetic. On the functional side, one of the reasons concerned itself with the potential that graphology has as a diagnostic tool for self observation and transformation. It can always be useful or interesting to know another's character, and often necessary; but it is far more soulful to know oneself, and from that knowledge initiate change if it is needed.

Graphology by its very nature is a two way street. We can relinquish or adopt specific writing forms and thereby shed what is limiting and obstructive and acquire what is strengthening and flowing. Still further we can work toward refinement of self, that we may considerately direct our own mark upon others.

Medical Graphology enhances the field, as mentioned before, by offering access to both physical and psychological states, by returning us to the esoteric roots of our letters and symbols and their spiritual content, and by embracing Chinese medicine and its innate search for Tao. It offers, in brief, the opportunity to practice extracting the holistic character out of the linear trait.

On the aesthetic side, I translated this book because I perceive and sense that graphology and the Eastern art of calligraphy — in all its variations — are reflections and degrees of one another. The reverent appreciation in the East for calligraphy's potential to express, through stroke, a person's quality of being is only a holistic form of graphology. And so, for the West to recognize and practice graphology is one way for it to begin perceiving not only a shared physical world, but a psychological and metaphysical one as well. In

Zen calligraphy we say: "If your mind is correct, the brush will be correct."[1]

In closing, I would like to extend a special thanks to J. M. Clarke for his help with my translation. I have also made every effort to credit the source for all material quoted in this book. If readers can provide any additional sources, please notify us in writing and we will be happy to note changes in future editions of the work.

C. C. Elian

---

[1]John Stevens, *Sacred Calligraphy of the East* (Boston, MA: Shambhala, 1988), p. 185.

Introduction

Graphology is the art of delineating human character by the study of handwriting. What does the word "character" mean? It has been defined as being the sum of the moral tendencies and qualities specific to an individual. According to most philosophies and many religions, human beings are made up of body, soul and spirit. The totality of these three elements — inseparable as long as we are on Earth — form the Being and participate in the formation of character. With this as our premise, keep in mind that, in graphology, we cannot separate the study of the soul from that of the body and the spirit.

However, many graphologists today only concern themselves with the study of one part of the character — psychological traits — without looking toward harmonizing or uniting the form and the content. For this reason I have turned to the great Chinese tradition and its medicine for my foundation. It is a fact that for thousands of years the Chinese have considered human beings as a totality. The Chinese hold that the three aspects (physical, psychological, and psychic) form a unity.

Contemporary science has proven that, where research is concerned, national boundaries do not exist, and that the basic elements are the same for all. It is not difficult to understand that in symbolism there are also no borders; there is neither East nor West, there is only one key common to all cultures.

As far as I know, only Eastern cultures have maintained the correspondences between the organs of the body, mind and spirit in their traditional medicine. This is the key we shall use in our study.

Most Western books on graphology analyze handwriting letter by letter. It's a linear approach that focuses primarily on the handwriter's psychological character. We will not be doing this. Because Eastern medicine is based on a holistic approach to the human being, so too will our approach to the alphabet be holistic.

First we will examine the basis of Chinese medicine. We will lay the groundwork for our graphological study by examining the circulation of energy throughout the being: we will be discussing the circulation of Chi; the meridians (which I call the 12 organ functions); yin and yang; and the four systems (digestive, respiratory, muscular, and cerebral).

We will then briefly take a look at each letter of the alphabet in order to establish each letter's correspondent in both the Hebrew and Egyptian hieroglyphic alphabets. This will allow us to look at each letter as a form—round, squat, open, closed or tall—and to examine the Hebrew and Egyptian correspondences so we can see the ancient and esoteric symbolism inherent in each form.

Then the main part of our study begins: we shall be examining closely each of the twelve organ functions (the meridians) and show how graphological analysis can be used as a diagnostic tool to look closely at the character of body, mind and spirit. And finally, we shall look at some examples that show medical graphology in practice.

1

The Chinese View
of the Human Body

This is not a medical textbook. I do not pretend to approach the question of Chinese medicine in all of its depth, nor to make a scientific and technical study, or even a philosophical one; many eminent physicians have already done so in detail, and many important references are listed in the bibliography of this book.

My goal is to grasp the essence of the Chinese spirit and philosophy in all of its refinement and subtlety, as well as the profundity of its psychology, and to make it comprehensible to the Western mentality, which is by nature, unaccustomed to this way of viewing the rhythm of life.

I will intentionally leave aside many details and specific points which, although being of great interest, have no direct bearing on this presentation of medical graphology; far from clarifying matters, they would only confuse us in our study.

This undertaking is therefore analogous to that of the scuba diver exploring the unknown but enormously rich depths of the ocean floor—it constitutes a first exploratory dive into Chinese medicine. The subsequent plunge will be up to you.

The Circulation of Energy

Life is like a wheel that never stops turning. Everything consists of unending cycles and rhythms. In the Chinese spirit it is illustrated in this way:

♦ Water falls from clouds onto the earth;

♦ The earth collects the water into lakes;

♦ Lakes feed the rivers;

♦ The rivers water the earth; receive other rivers, then flow into the sea;

♦ The sea receives this water, impresses upon it its own rhythm, submits it to its laws;

♦ The water evaporates into the air;

♦ The air condenses the water into clouds;

♦ The clouds water the earth.

Humankind is not exempt from these laws, for the microcosm is a reflection of the macrocosm.

According to Chinese thought, the microcosm is animated by a current of energy called Chi, an incorporeal fluid which is to the life of the being as the soul and spirit are to the body. This circulation of energy, which is entire unto itself, regulates the body down to its smallest cells; outwardly, it sensitizes certain points on the body which the Chinese have connected by imaginary lines called meridians. (See figures 1 and 2 on pages 3, 4. In Chinese medicine, this predetermined path of energy circulation is considered to work in a perpetual immutable cycle throughout the day and night as long as the Being lives.[1] In keeping with the image of the microcosm as macrocosm:

---

[1]The cycle is: the lung meridian, the large intestine, the stomach, the spleen-pancreas, the heart, the small intestine, the bladder, the kidneys, circulation-sexuality, the triple heater, the gall bladder and the liver.

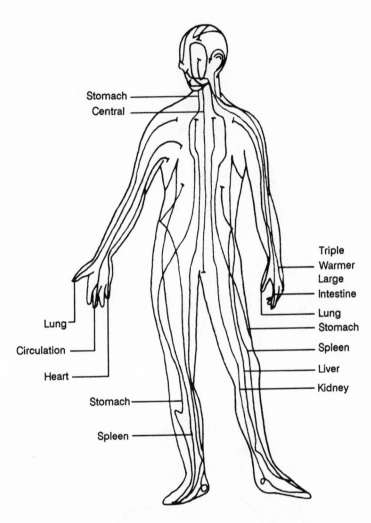

Figure 1. The meridians are predetermined paths of energy circulation. The paths are shown on the front of the body. (Adapted from Toward Balance *by Rita McNamara, p. 6.)*

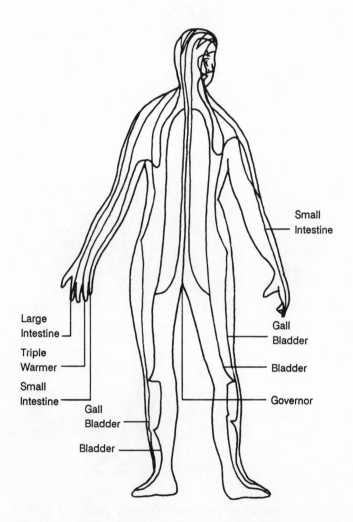

*Figure 2.   The meridians look this way on the back of the body.
(Adapted from* Toward Balance *by Rita McNamara, p. 7.)*

♦ The water falls upon the earth: air enters into the Being (lungs) and determines the rate of chemical processes, the energy coming from the outside — while matter in its fashion then regulates this entry (large intestine).

♦ The earth collects the water in its lakes: the organism accepts this nourishment (stomach) coming from the outside and stores (spleen-pancreas) the material energy which it represents in reserves which will serve to structure its form.

♦ The lakes feed the rivers; the blood (heart) circulates the energy throughout the organism's tissues.

♦ The rivers water the earth, receive other rivers, then flow into the sea; this circulation of energy and influx from the exterior brings life to the inner organs, which then come into play. Some bring to the individual strength (kidneys) and specific form (small intestine), while others eliminate that which is unnecessary, like a river deposits silt along its banks (bladder).

♦ The sea receives this water, impresses upon it its own rhythm, submits it to its laws; the energy has attained its maximum intensity and balance, yet it is in constant flow. Its power will enable the individual on the one hand to release through sexual and mental procreation (mental forms are sexual functions at a higher level), and on the other, to survive despite this "loss" of energy by bringing back to the center from the periphery the flow of blood that had left it (circulation-sexuality).

♦ The water evaporates into the air: all delicate instruments are sensitive to temperature, and we are no exception to this law. The temperature of the body must remain constant (triple heater).

And so, as the sun acts upon the sea through evaporation, the energy at this stage transforms itself into a current of energetic fire that gives physical and psychic power by

ascending to the brain along the spinal cord; and here ends
our similarity to animals (who do not stand erect, for in them
the rising current does not exist).

♦ The air condenses water into clouds: that which has rip-
ened and been worked on in close quarters at high temperature produces stench and decay. Thus, there is bile, the
"condensation" of this gall (gall bladder). As the fertilizer
is extracted from compost, so the gall bladder will transform what it has been given into new energy, which will
soon be concentrated (liver) and integrated into the organism to give it tone. Mentally, the individual thinks and
creates.

♦ The clouds water the earth: under the pressure of heat, in
this process of the concentration of matter (liver), an outlet for aeration is necessary and does exist (lungs). An
outlet for exhalation, this passage is also used for inhalation, a reminder that the rhythm of this vital energetic
current is without end. It is necessary to breathe and eat in
order to live.

Before beginning the study of the role of these meridians
relative to the organs of the body and their psychological
implications, we will briefly look at how Chinese ideas on the
circulation of energy are related to the major streams of
philosophical thought. This cycle of involution-evolution,
this ascending and descending current of energy, the union of
spirit and matter, this Oneness is found in all religions.

For example, the Christian religion invites us to meditate
on the themes from the Holy Scriptures. From the very
beginning, the Bible shows the desire of Adam and Eve to
draw on the source of knowledge, to become equal to God,
and therefore obliged to go through the digestive cycle (the
apple) and then through that of sexuality, "they saw that they
were naked."

Who gave them the fruit? The serpent, symbol of Knowledge a) curled at the base of the tree represents curiosity, the desire to know; b) curled below the feet of the Virgin who subdued it, it symbolizes material knowledge under the control of spiritual knowledge; c) biting its tail, it has accomplished the cycle of matter, comparable to that of the Chinese circulation, and in having transformed matter into energy it rejoins spirit—true knowledge has been acquired.

Tantra views this circulation of energy in the form of kundalini, which activates the chakras as it rises. The Hebrew Kabbalah calls it the Shekinah, which illuminates the Sephiroth. And we find in the eleventh chapter of Lao Tzu:

Thirty spokes unite around the nave;
From their not-being (loss of individuality)
Arises the utility of the wheel.
Mold clay into a vessel;
From its not-being (in the vessel's hollow)
Arises the utility of the vessel.
Cut out doors and windows in the house (a wall),
From their not-being (empty space) arises the
    utility of the house.
Therefore by the existence of things we profit,
And by the non-being of things we are served.[2]

This circulation of energy makes it impossible to conceive of disassociating the study of the body from that of the soul. That is why Chinese medicine indissolubly combines the physical, the psychological and the psychical. On this point it is in complete opposition to our Western mentality, which tends more and more to specialize itself by studying each organ separately.

Consider though, that while we consult a laryngologist for our throats, a cardiologist for our hearts or a psycholo-

---

[2]This English translation is from *The Wisdom of Laotse*, translated and edited by Lin Yutang (New York: The Modern Library, 1948).

gist for our character, we would never think of consulting a specialist for the carburetor of our car and another for the pistons. It cannot be overstated that we are a totality, no part of which can be studied in isolation.

The teachings of the Western tradition inform us that the letters of the alphabet symbolize physical organs and parts of the body.[3] Thus each letter will correspond to:

♦ a meridian (or organ);

♦ a quality (physical and psychological);

♦ a flaw (physical and psychological);

♦ a psychic state.

This will give us the key to medical graphology according to the psychology of the organs of the Chinese meridians.

Yin and Yang

Chinese tradition teaches us through Taoist thought that all natural phenomena are the result of the polarity of two principles, two opposite forces, each of which is transformable into the other:

♦ the yin — negative, feminine;

♦ the yang — positive, masculine.

The yin brings death, cold, darkness, meditation, substance; it is a lunar and interior force. The yang brings life, heat, light, movement, energy; it is a solar and exterior force. Yin is concentration and Yang expansion.

Phenomenal life results from the interaction of these two current-forces. The constantly disrupted balance must unceasingly be re-established in a perpetual movement, for if

---

[3]See *Nouveau Guide de Graphologie* by Marguerite de Surany (Paris: Nouvelles Editions Debresse, 1958), p. 21. *Tr.*

there is imbalance, the result will be psychic and physical disorder which eventually leads to illness.

In the *Tao Te Ching*, Lao Tsu tells us:

> Under heaven all can see beauty as beauty only because there is ugliness.
> All can know good as good only because there is evil.
> Therefore having and not having arise together.
> Difficult and easy complement each other.
> Long and short contrast each other;
> High and low rest upon each other;
> Voice and sound harmonize each other;
> Front and back follow one another.[4]

The 12 Organ-Functions

The Chinese call imaginary lines running throughout the entire body along known pathways, meridians. These meridians are currents of yin and yang energy,[5] and they all have organic correspondences. We will not take up the study of the pathways of the meridians; it would only complicate matters without adding anything to our knowledge of graphology. We will concentrate instead on how the meridians correspond with the organs of the body as the 12 organ-functions. Here they are in the sequence of the circulation of energy in the circadian cycle: lungs, large intestine, stomach, spleen-pancreas, heart, small intestine, bladder, kidneys, circulation-sexuality, triple heater, gall bladder, and liver.

---

[4]Lao Tsu, *Tao Te Ching*, translated by Gia-Fu Feng and Jane English (New York: Alfred A. Knopf, 1974) #2.

[5]The energy is said to flow in a circle from one meridian to another in definite succession, without cease as long as there is life, according to Dr. Niboyet in *Essai sur l'Acupuncture Chinoise Pratique* (Paris: Editions Dominique Wapler, 1951), p. 15. The translation is mine. *Tr.*

"Circulation-sexuality" and "triple heater" are typically Chinese functions. That is to say: in nature there is that which can be touched, that which is tangible, but that which is subtle also exists. One does not go without the other. By analogy we can say that circulation-sexuality can be seen as being peripheral circulation, or the projection of kundalini along the spinal cord. The triple heater is the regulatory system which, through appropriate contractions, circulates the energy in the canals either slower or faster.

Each organ-function is connected to a psychological cause and its operation is a factor in the activity of the psyche. Chinese thought expresses it as a subtle interplay that is as amazing by its poetry as it is by its reality. I will not here describe all of the laws of the mechanism by which these twelve organ functions operate; there are many, and you as a graphologist are free to look into them for yourself.

Throughout this book we will focus on two factors which seem to have opened some very large perspectives. They are:

1. *The factory/treasury principle*: the organs are paired two by two. In each couple, one is called "the factory" and the other "the treasury." They are to be studied as a pair, each in relation to the other.

The factory organs are yang. They draw their energy from the exterior and transform into blood—and so into energy—the nutrition, air, and prana which they receive. They are active.

The treasury organs are yin. They receive their energy independently of the exterior. They purify and circulate the blood. They are passive agents.

Chapter 4 will provide a detailed presentation of the application of this principle in graphology.

2. *The husband/wife principle*: certain organ-functions are husband, others are wife. This principle expresses a harmony between two organ functions, similar to that of a trine

between two planets in an astrological chart.[6] You may already have foreseen that this can indicate the psychological result of a husband organ-function oppressing a wife organ function (or vice versa).

"And the Chinese add that the husband must be powerful, that is to say, at least more powerful than the wife, and the wife flexible and a little weaker than the husband."[7] The application of this principle in graphology will come up in chapter 4.

The Four Systems

According to Nei-Ching: "Man possesses four seas and the twelve meridians are like the rivers which come to throw themselves into these four seas. The four seas are: the sea of Nourishment, the sea of Blood, the sea of Energy, and the sea of the Medulla."[8] Chinese medicine therefore recognizes 4 systems:

♦ the digestive system — nourishment;

♦ the respiratory system — blood;

♦ the muscular system — energy;

♦ the cerebral system — spinal cord and brain.

As the four blades of a windmill are made to turn by the force of the wind, these four systems are put into motion thanks to a fifth one called the circulatory system.

---

[6]When two planets are in a 120 degree angular relationship (a trine) they express harmony.

[7]From Niboyet, *Essai sur l'Acupuncture Chinoise Pratique*, p. 180. The translation is mine. *Tr.*

[8]From an undated essay entitled *Traité sur L'Intelligence et Subtilité des Rapports Secrets (entre les 4 Systèmes)* by A. Chamfrault. No English translation.

And here is where that Chinese subtlety so valuable to us in psychology comes in: the circulatory system is not a "sea" into which the currents throw themselves — it is their *soul*.

"And the soul," says the Nei-Ching, "dwells in the heart." Within the four systems the organ-functions each have a definite role to play among, and in relation to each other. We should point out that the role of the organ-function in a system will not necessarily be the same when it involves a different cycle; we will return to this subject in the following chapters, which provide detailed tables to help avoid mistakes or unnecessary research.[9]

Those who have played Mah-Jong know the apparent simplicity of this game which, if we wish to bring it to a satisfactory conclusion, requires subtle combinations of the kind that Westerners have come to attribute to the Chinese mind. We encounter the same subtlety here and should not be surprised to see that certain organ-functions play alternatively the role of husband or wife, or more precisely, are yin or yang according to the system in which we observe them. This aspect of Chinese medicine and philosophy may at first seem unusual, but it is also to be found in Hebrew philosophy (the teachings of the Kabbalah). In fact, if a given sephira is *negative* relative to the one from which it emanates, it is *positive* relative to the one which it itself emanates.

---

[9]Dr. Choain, *Voie Rationelle de la Médecine Chinoise* (Lille, France: Editions S.I.E.L., 1957). The translation is mine. *Tr.* The Nei-Ching is the text of the Yellow Emperor. For more on Nei-Ching see *Yellow Emperor's Classic of Internal Medicine*, translated by Ilza Veith (Berkeley, CA: University of California Press, 1972); and Ted Kaptchuk, *The Web That Has No Weaver* (New York: Congdon & Weed, 1983).

2

Graphology from A to Z

To avoid any misunderstanding concerning graphology, we will begin with some basics. First of all, I would like to stress the fact that although we are going to focus upon the forms of the letters like a watchmaker examining the parts of a watch, under no circumstances will we forget that the first concern of the graphologist must be with the totality of the handwriting—just as the medical doctor should make it a point to discern the personality of the patients who come for diagnosis.

I would like to insist upon this point all the more so because it will not be repeated. Every graphologist is aware of this primary consideration. But what many have not done is to relate each organ to a letter in order to extract medical and psychological information: this will be the only method used in this book. We are not out to split hairs or to belabor trifles, but in medical practice it is precisely the details, the trifles, that elucidate the results of an overall examination.

Some readers' ideas may be shaken because they have studied a classical perspective of graphology. These readers should realize the nature of the terrain upon which they have ventured: *Medical Graphology* is a precise undertaking that involves both deduction and intuition. It must be done with knowledge, understanding, and love.

The graphologist will have to pay attention to a number of basic concepts:

1. *The shape of a letter or its formation*. The child learns to write the alphabet according to a set model, then as the personality comes more into play, the initial form will gradually be changed. We take this transformation into account and it constitutes the most important part of our work. If the letterform conforms to the standard model, we will know that the corresponding organ is not defective. If this is not the case, we will view it as a "flaw" with its various psychological consequences.

2. *Openings in a letter*. In the shape of a letter, the form and location of any opening should be noted. For example, an *o* normally is closed: if the writer leaves a break at the top, the interpretation of that letter will be different from one whose opening is at the bottom. The same reasoning applies if this break is to the right or to the left. As a general rule:

♦ When the opening is at the top, we will adopt the Chinese terminology and call it a *yang* opening.

♦ On the other hand, an opening at the bottom will be called a *yin* opening. For example:

$$\mathcal{Cv} = \text{this } a \text{ is yang}$$
$$\mathcal{Q} = \text{this } a \text{ is yin}$$

As you may know, the *yang current* is solar and corresponds to the blood and to physical life, whereas the *yin current* is lunar and corresponds to the life of the nerves and to energy; the meaning of the letter *a* will therefore be completely different if its opening, which ought to be a yang (in a normal script the "a" is started at the top), has transformed itself into yin. The solar plexus (*a*) is supposed to radiate light and warmth: if it becomes reflected by the lunar spirit then we are dealing with a mentality that is at variance with the norm.

3. *The filling-in of a letter.* A blocked letter is one where a loop or the body of the letter itself is filled-in with ink. Everyone knows that to block a clear area and render it opaque is to obscure it, to alter the function of the object. In graphology we know that the *l* should have an open loop. Knowing that this letter corresponds to the liver,[1] we understand right away that the ink is the bile that chokes it.

4. *Transformation of a letter.* Many writers modify the form of a letter to the point where a reader might confuse it with another. Therefore an *n* might be changed into a *u*, or a *t* into a *v*. This shows that the organ that corresponds to the transformed letter is fulfilling its role improperly, and no doctor can deny that an organ that functions to the detriment, or in place of another, is bound to create some damage. For example, there is the case where breathing is accomplished through the mouth instead of the nose; or where the digestive functions are disturbed by a shortage of saliva, and so the digestive process incompletely begun in the mouth requires a greater activity from the pancreas. The psychologist also understands the harm that may be done by "undigested" and "badly assimilated" ideas.

5. *Additional letters.* Their addition is no more to be overlooked than, say, stones that become lodged in the kidneys.

6. *Omitted letters.* Their omission is not due to chance or absent-mindedness, but rather to the fatigue and exhaustion of the corresponding organ, along with its psychological consequences.

7. *Letter of a larger size than its neighbor.* This situation indicates the importance that the writer accords to the idea or to the organ that the letter represents. The sentimentalist will trace his *a*'s, and the jovian his *d*'s.

---

[1] We will go into more depth on the correspondences in the next chapter; this is used here simply as an example.

The reduction in size of a letter has a similar significance. In the handwriting of someone with intestinal trouble, the *p* (which corresponds to the intestines) is diminished in its descending stroke. It is rare that a male homosexual will have strongly traced *i*'s and *j*'s (YOD = masculine principle).

8. *Letter connections*. As a result of organic deficiency, we have seen letters that relate to unhealthy organs isolated in the middle of a word.

9. *Rhythm*. The rhythm of the strokes of the letters needs to be observed. If a letter within a text maintains its form, this indicates that its meaning — good or bad — is invariable and that we are faced with an established fact. But if the form is different throughout, we will conclude that there is accidental weakness, a crisis, or the beginning of an illness.

I think it possible to affirm that *spelling mistakes do not exist*: if we study closely the pattern of the errors, we will notice that it's always the same letters that are omitted, added, or inverted. For example, a very secretive adolescent replaced all of the *r*'s (RESH = speech) with *s*'s (SAMECH = the secret). Another young French boy, writing to a 16-year-old girlfriend and hiding this from his parents, would finish each letter with these words: "en t'ebrassat" (literally: "kissing you" = correctly spelled = "en t'e*m*brassa*n*t"). He had therefore omitted the *m* and the *n*, which, respectively, represent his mother (MEM) and his father (NUN); he would rather not have them as witnesses to his kisses.

A woman, obsessed by her liver disease, did not miss a chance to double her *l*'s (LAMED = the liver), or to add them to the *p*'s and the *r*'s, giving them a bizarre shape. If we consider that the *l* LAMED corresponds to the sense of self-sacrifice, it comes as no surprise to learn that this woman was convinced that she was constantly being sacrificed to others.

An adolescent in full puberty was placing *c*'s wherever he could, not hesitating to replace *s*'s with *c*'s. The *c* is the hand that takes and holds; this young man, very disoriented by his coming of age, would take various objects in the house and collect them in his room, thus proving his manhood and his new power of acquisition and possession.

A young woman who had never known her father could never write the letter *i* (YOD) and had to reread her text in order to "add" it. YOD is the creative masculine principle.

In medical graphology, everything must be noted or taken into account. Every indication is a clinical sign, nothing is the result of chance and everything has a meaning — it is up to us to see it.

Keeping this in mind, let's now take a look at each letter of the Latin alphabet in order to establish its correspondences in the Hebrew and Egyptian hieroglyphic alphabets, as well as to the Tarot.

The millenia-old teachings of tradition have left us the key to the secret meaning of the Hebrew letters, which, themselves, have their origin in the Egyptian hieroglyphs as I understand it. All occult sources are open to question, but if all the teachings agree on some points, then doubt is no longer possible.

Starting with the constants given by tradition, we will make a junction between East and West, in this and the next chapter, by considering concurrently Chinese medicine and its Taoist principles, the Latin alphabet, the Hebrew alphabet, the Egyptian hieroglyphs, and the 22 major arcana of the Tarot. We will see that East and West are governed by a single teaching accessible by a same key; it is more imaged for the Middle East, and more dialectical in the West and in China. Our key is the letter and its form, hence graphological analysis.

It seems fitting at this point to quote from *The Mystical Qabalah* by Dion Fortune, who states that:

> . . . correct attributions fit upon the Tree through
> endless ramifications of symbolism, as we saw when

considering Binah as the Mother; incorrect symbolism breaks down and reveals its bizarre associations
at the first attempt to follow out a chain of correspondences. It is amazing what ramifications of
association-chains can be followed when the attri-
bution is correct. It seems as if it were only the
extent of our knowledge which limits the length of
the chain that can be linked logically together; it
will extend through science, art, mathematics, and
the epochs of history; through ethics, psychology,
and physiology. It was this particular method of
using the mind which in all probability gave the
ancients their premature knowledge of natural science, knowledge which has to await the invention of
instruments of precision for its confirmation.[2]

---

[2]Dion Fortune, *The Mystical Qabalah* (York Beach, ME: Samuel Weiser, 1984;
and Wellingborough, England: Thorsons Publishing Group, 1984), p. 51.

Practical Application of A[3]

A represents:

- ◆ Love;
- ◆ Sentimentality;
- ◆ Chastity;
- ◆ Faith;
- ◆ Imagination;
- ◆ Vanity;
- ◆ The solar plexus.

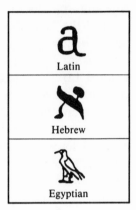

In Hebrew, *A* = ALEPH and the eagle in Egyptian heiroglyphics. *A* corresponds to the 1st arcanum, the Magician.

ALEPH is full of sun and light. Whether or not a person is spiritual or materialistic, to that degree they will notice these qualities.

The Egyptian ALEPH is represented by the eagle which soars to the heights, toward the sun. This bird symbolizes light and intelligence. A child who does well in school is called an eagle: his eyes see what others cannot. And many countries have chosen the eagle as an emblem to indicate their own supremacy!

In the *a* we will find the quality of love, the quest for self elevation, and, at the same time, vanity. The openings found in this letter will indicate from which direction the writer seeks satisfaction. When the *a* (this principle is valid for all of

---

[3]Much of this material that appears in this section was previously published in my book, *Guide de Graphologie Moderne*, published by Guy Trédaniel, Editions de la Maisnie, 76, rue Claude-Bernard, 75005 Paris.

the letters) is open toward the top (the sun, yang), emotional aspirations and imagination are idealistic. When the *a* opens at the bottom (the moon, yin), it indicates that feelings are colored more by sensuality and materialism, but does not rule out spirituality. When the opening is toward the left, toward the Self, the writer's feelings and imagination draw upon the joys of the past and their remembrance rather than upon what is in the present. An opening toward the right, toward Life, indicates someone who seeks out new adventures and looks forward to the future.

On another level, ALEPH corresponds to the Magician in the Tarot. When the *a* is simply written without ornament or inner loops, it indicates someone who, like the Magician, has risen above vanity and needs to deal with it no longer. Exaggerated self-importance, on the other hand, is indicated by an *a* that is large, often written in script form, thereby becoming even more noticeable.

ALEPH is also chastity and love on an emotional level. Its shape and opening represent wherefrom the writer seeks and finds love. Additionally, let us remember that ALEPH in Egyptian hieroglyphs represents the Light Principle.

A large *a* represents:

♦ In a sensual handwriting, a quest for ever new sensations;

♦ In a mental handwriting, the search for intellectual knowledge;

♦ In an elementary handwriting, it is the Light of love in all of its simplicity.

However, in an evolved handwriting, the quest for spiritual light no longer expresses itself by way of enlargement of the letter *a*, which, like all other letters in such a handwriting, maintains a normal and harmonious appearance.

Practical Application of B

B represents:

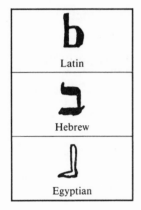

♦ Inner work which allows us
to elevate ourselves through
wisdom or else to limit
through suffering;

♦ The stomach which digests
nutrients in the same way
that thought assimilates
ideas;

♦ The left eye (inner
reflection).

B corresponds to the 2nd arcanum, the High Priestess.

B = BETH in the Hebrew alphabet. The Zohar states
that, when the Almighty wished to create the world, the letters presented themselves one by one before the throne in
order to attain the honor of being the first letter of the Holy
Scriptures, the eventual material of the Book of Genesis. One
by one they lauded their qualities and brought up reasons to
be chosen. After reviewing them all, God called forth the
letter BETH, *b*, to preside over the Holy Scriptures because
this letter represented the Word, the nascent Verb. Thus the
text of Genesis begins with the word *Bereshith*, meaning in
the beginning.

Practical Application of C

C represents:

- Strength in its physical aspect;
- Acquisition;
- The right eye;
- Life and death.

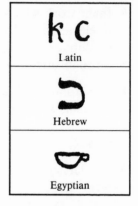

C = KAPH, the hand which takes, which seizes and holds. This letter represents life as opposed to death. *C* corresponds to the 11th arcanum, Justice.

Practical Application of D

D represents:

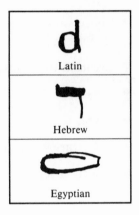

Latin

Hebrew

Egyptian

♦ Inner rectitude;

♦ Judgment;

♦ Fertility, sterility and goodness;

♦ Organization;

♦ Professional activity (money and all the means of attaining it);

♦ The gall bladder;

♦ The right nostril.

D = DALETH, the source of all physical existence. It represents fertility or sterility. It is the gavel of justice which judges and decides. *D* corresponds to the 4th arcanum, the Emperor.

Practical Application of E

E represents:

♦ Impressionability,
  receptivity;

♦ Creation of forms;

♦ Breath;

♦ Hope;

♦ The ovaries and the testicles;

♦ The right leg.

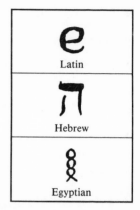

E = HE, inhalation and breathing, the Breath. In the tetra-gram YOD-HE-WAW-HE, the HE represents the Cosmic Egg which, fertilized by way of YOD, the Creative Masculine Principle, gives birth to the WAW, the *v*, the light, and becomes Breath. It is also the chalice which receives the impressions of the external world as gathered by the senses. *E* corresponds to the 5th arcanum, the Hierophant.

Practical Application of F

F represents:

♦ Degree of attachment to the
mother. It should be studied
in conjunction with the letter
m (*m* = MEM = the
Mother) and with the left
margin (the past, mother,
family and self).

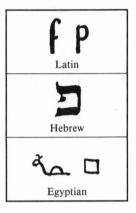

F = PE, physical creation, or procreation. It is the masculine
seed which fertilizes the female egg. It indicates the manifestation of individualized being: "I am." *F* corresponds to the
17th arcanum, the Star.

At birth, a third party cuts the umbilical cord by which
the child is linked to the mother. It is the first natural manifestation of individualized being. Around age 7, the child
learns how to write and how to form an *f* with its upper loop
mirroring its lower one. The child at that stage loses his baby
teeth and attains the age of reasoning.

By age 14, adolescents become aware of themselves; it is
the second natural manifestation of individualization. They
seek to conceptually separate from the maternal matrix. In
order to achieve this they rebel: the *f*'s change form, the
lower loop turns back toward the left and forms the continuous figure eight. This rebelliousness is indicated as long as the
letterform's direction is inverted.

As a rule, at 21 (three times seven and the age at which
we attain legal majority), the adolescent consciously becomes

adult and, delivered from childhood and mother, is initiated into the spiritual life and thereby that of creativity. The letterform *f* resumes its standard appearance and, generally speaking, the lower loop is then replaced by a simple vertical stroke.

Practical Application of G

G represents:

♦ Assimilation and transmutation of nutrients and of ideas;

♦ Satisfaction or dissatisfaction with Self;

♦ Wealth, poverty, caution;

♦ The sensation of acceptance or of rejection;

♦ The throat;

♦ The right ear.

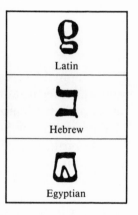

Latin

Hebrew

Egyptian

G is either wealth or poverty. Because of its correspondence with the throat, it also signifies the assimilation of nutrients and ideas — assimilation which results in either satisfaction or dissatisfaction.

G = GIMEL, a camel or an open hand that takes. *G* corresponds to the 3rd arcanum, the Empress.

Practical Application of H

H represents:

- ◆ Sociability;
- ◆ Humility;
- ◆ The balance within effort;
- ◆ Breath;
- ◆ The lungs;
- ◆ The right arm;
- ◆ Sight.

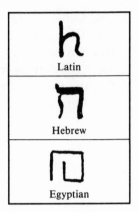

H = HETH, the work to be done through the "use of the transformative powers of matter." It is the balance within effort. Human and social contact is part of our field of experience; we must give but also must accept and receive. *H* corresponds to the 8th arcanum, Strength.

Practical Application of I

I represents:

♦ The father of the writer, and
his or her own attitude
towards authority (also study
the right margin which signifies the future, the father
and others).

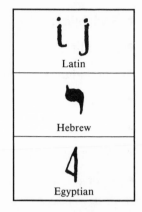

I = YOD, commandment, active and manifest unity, the
extended finger. *I* corresponds to the 10th arcanum, the
Wheel of Fortune.

Practical Application of J

J represents:

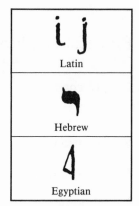

Latin

Hebrew

Egyptian

♦ Activity;

♦ Commandments;

♦ The active, creative masculine power;

♦ Reason;

♦ The left arm;

♦ The male sexual organ.

J = YOD is the positive, creative, masculine principle. It is the realized Self, bearer of the Divine Spark. The form of the YOD is that of the Egyptian reed tool with which they traced the hieroglyphs. *J* corresponds to the 10th arcanum, the Wheel of Fortune.

Practical Application of K

K is related to *C* and has the same associations.

Practical Application of L

L represents:

♦ Expansion;

♦ Possession;

♦ Elaboration of plans;

♦ Discernment;

♦ Sacrifice;

♦ Egotism;

♦ Aggression;

♦ The liver.

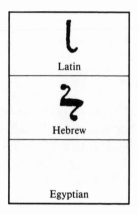

Latin

Hebrew

Egyptian

L = LAMED, the symbol of the extended arm, of the bird's wing and of all which unfolds. Some people can be giving to the point of renunciation and sacrifice, yet others contract and refuse to reach out, refuse to give. It is then self-centeredness. *L* corresponds to 12th arcanum, the Hanged Man.

Practical Application of M

M represents:

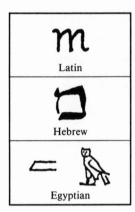

Latin

Hebrew

Egyptian

♦ The Mother (also study the
  letter *f* and the left margin);

♦ Death;

♦ Destruction;

♦ Rebirth;

♦ The matrix.

M = MEM. Whereas ALEPH is symbolized by the eagle and
by light, MEM corresponds to the owl, the bird of night and
solitude. It is at night, during its silence, that we can meditate
and attain liberation. It is within the night, in water and in
silence, that the fetus develops. MEM also corresponds to the
mother, the matrix, to water. However, it also relates to death
since the physical life which the mother gives to the child
contains inevitably the seed of death. *M* corresponds to the
13th arcanum, Death.

Practical Application of N

N represents:

◆ The father (also study the *i*
  and the right margin);

◆ Psychic balance;

◆ The nose, smell;

◆ The male genitals;

◆ The bladder.

N = NUN, the fruit, the product, and the result. "It is the natural outcome initiated by the masculine seed when it reaches the fruit of the female urnes," says J. R. Legrand.[4] It is a symbol of continuity and passiveness. *N* corresponds to the 14th arcanum, Temperance.

---

[4]J. R. LeGrand was a Parisian lecturer and student of esoteric subjects who I interviewed in 1964.

Practical Application of O

O represents:

♦ Matter;

♦ Anger, pride;

♦ That which is false, devious, perverted, or evil;

♦ The liver (however, the *l* gives the best indications as to this organ's condition).

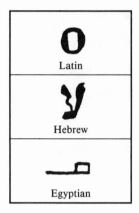

Whereas LAMED (*l*) represents sacrifice willingly undertaken, AYIN (*o*) represents sacrifice which is imposed and to which one submits. It is death in its physical aspect. *O* corresponds to the 16th arcanum, the Tower.

Practical Application of P

P represents:

- Speech;
- Sensitivity, discernment;
- Finances;
- Domination, enslavement;
- The intestines;
- The left ear.

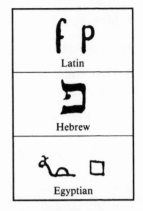

P = PE, a symbol for the mouth by which we express our thoughts. It is the verb in action, the soul linking Matter to Spirit. *P* corresponds to the 17th arcanum, the Star.

Practical Application of Q

Q represents:

♦ The intelligence of ideas;

♦ Laughter;

♦ Force, constraint;

♦ The spleen.

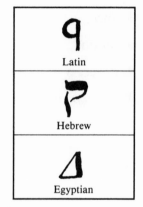

Q = QOPH, a cutting instrument, all that serves as a tool for people, that which defends and assists us. KAPH (*c*) is the hand which takes, which holds and retains. It is the container wherein occurs the blend of forces. QOPH Is compression, force, constraint. It is that matter which we are to work upon. *Q* corresponds to the 19th arcanum, the Sun.

Practical Application of R

R represents:

♦ Speech;

♦ Motion;

♦ Peace, war;

♦ The left nostril.

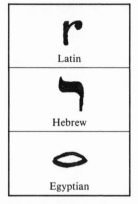

R = RESH, the symbol of motion. It corresponds to the head inasmuch as the head commands the movements. It also represents the mouth by which nourishment enters and out of which exits speech. *R* corresponds to the 20th arcanum, Judgment.

Practical Application of S

S represents:

Latin

Hebrew

Egyptian

♦ The turning in towards self;

♦ Secrecy;

♦ Egotism;

♦ Money earned and gathered;

♦ Sleep.

In the Latin alphabet, there is only one *s*, and both Hebrew letters SHIN and SAMEKH correspond to it. However, at an esoteric level, there is a vast difference between these two *s*'s. SAMEKH symbolized motion that returns to the point of departure. This movement signifies the struggle of turning inward toward the seed — thereby representing the instinctive forces which draw us toward matter. Those who are familiar with the Tarot will understand why the card associated with this letter is that of the Devil, the Typhon. SHIN, on the other hand, symbolizes balance as well as rising fire. The three upward lines of its form easily evoke this association.

SAMEKH and SHIN both represent the circle: SAMEKH is the concrete circle — as shown by its design; SHIN is the circle of the ideal surrounded by flames. SAMEKH is that which is below and draws toward matter; SHIN is that which is above and draws toward the spiritual.

S corresponds to the 15th arcanum, the Devil.

Practical Application of T

There are two very important aspects of the *t* to study: the horizontal stroke and the vertical stroke.

The *t*'s vertical stroke represents:

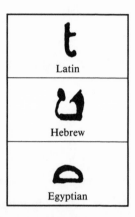

◆ The roof, security;

◆ Mental concentration (the result of which is psychic balance, the horizontal bar of the *t*);

◆ Decision;

◆ Will or fear;

◆ Nerves;

◆ Physical stamina;

◆ Hearing;

◆ The right kidney.

The vertical stroke of *t* corresponds to TETH — the shield, the concept of resistance. However, it also symbolizes alliance, the unifying action, the possession of things. It corresponds to the 9th arcanum, the Hermit.

The *t*'s horizontal bar represents:

♦ The roof, the soul;

♦ Psychic and vital balance;

♦ Emotion;

♦ Formation of consciousness;

♦ Beauty, ugliness;

♦ The heart.

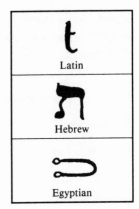

The horizontal bar corresponds to TAW, the principle of balance. It is the essence of life. It also corresponds to the 21st arcanum, the World.

Practical Application of U, V

U and *v* were once the same letter. We will concern ourselves, graphologically speaking, only with the letter *v*.
V represents:

♦ Self-determination;

♦ Patience;

♦ Authority;

♦ Will, whose origin is in meditation;

♦ The left kidney.

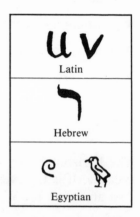

V = WAW, the understanding of that which is Self and that which is not Self: it is self-determination. It symbolizes justice. It is the rod of authority as well as an agent of alliance. It corresponds to the 6th arcanum, the Lovers.

Practical Application of W

W is derived from *v*. In French it is called double *v* as opposed to double *u* in English. The associations are the same for *u*, *v* and *w*.

Practical Application of X

X represents:

♦ The gestation of the fetus, including its receptivity to all of the sensations undergone by the mother, which will affect the child's first reactions to life;

♦ The source of ideas.

The letter *x* has no correspondence in the Hebrew alphabet or in the Tarot. In the Egyptian hieratic alphabet it seems to correspond to the sound KH, which is the mysterious movement of cosmic forces combining in a specific way to create the phenomenon of life. Please note that when the *x* is handwritten it is composed of an *s* and a *c*. The *s* is the secret; the *c* is the container where the blend takes place.

Practical Application of Y

Y is related to *i*. The associations are the same.

Practical Application of Z

Z represents:

- ◆ Action, movement;
- ◆ Victory, justice;
- ◆ Sexuality;
- ◆ The left leg.

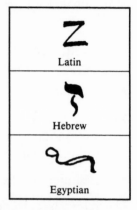

Z = ZAYIN, the moving serpent. It represents swiftness, the journey, and all that is distant. *Z* has two correspondences in Tarot: the 7th arcanum, the Chariot, and the 18th arcanum, the Moon.

3

The Twelve Organ Functions

We will now examine each organ function separately in order to unveil its secret and see what role it plays in the organism and its reflection on the psychological and psychic levels. This information should enable readers to acquire the necessary flexibility and vision to understand the motivating spirit behind this graphological study according to traditional Chinese medicine. Students should also remember that when letters deviate from their normal configuration, it is not unlikely for them to look like another one; within the context of a word, the letter will look more like what it is supposed to be. Out of context, though, each letter we discuss has only its form to stand on.

Before using the scalpel, the surgeon learns to handle it with care. The graphological samples that we will use for each organ function have all been verified; but I stress the fact that although it is fruitful to examine an organ to locate its weakness, this is useless if the organ in question is examined alone and not in relation to its colleagues. Accordingly I will restate at the beginning of the study of each organ function its principle role in the yin/yang interaction within the flow of energy.

On the pages listed below you will find the 12 organ functions classified in the sequence of the flow of energy through the day/night cycle, with their graphological correspondences:

The Heart

Function: The heart is a yin treasury organ (its yang factory organ is the large intestine). The heart is husband (its wife are the lungs).

Latin
letter: *t* (horizontal bar only).

Hebrew
letter: TAU Principle of balance, sign of sympathy.[1]

---

[1]The Hebrew is from Fabre d'Olivet's *The Hebraic Tongue Restored* (1921; reprinted York Beach, ME: Samuel Weiser, Inc., 1981, 1991).

Egyptian
hieroglyph: The ancient Egyptians[2] consecrated Tau to
                Thoth and considered it the symbol of the uni-
                versal soul.[3]

Tarot: 21st major arcanum, the World.

Role of the Heart

The heart lets in the outer environment's energy (oxygen) into
the inner environment. It is the orchestral conductor of all
cellular circulatory movements and of the sensitivity of the
epidermis. George Soulié de Morant defined it in this way:
"The heart is the Minister of the Lord and Master; when it is
firm and solid, troubles do not enter easily. It is the essence
of life."[4]

And Ch'I-Po told the Yellow Emperor, "The heart is like
the minister of the monarch who excels through insight and
understanding."[5]

Psychology

The heart is the principle of balance and of life. All movement to create a balanced life must be ordered, rhythmic,
harmonious, and wise.

How does disorder introduce itself? By the passions, but
also through too much passivity, which is really a sign of
indifference. The psychic reflection of the heart is sensitivity,
affectivity, consciousness, emotivity.

---

[2]The Egyptian in this section is from Enel's *La Langue Sacrée* (Paris: Editions Maisonneuve-La Rose, 1984).

[3]The Chinese say, "And the soul is lodged in the heart."

[4]The definitions of Soulié de Morant are quoted in Dr. Choain, *Voie Rationelle de la Medecine Chinoise Pratique*, p. 455. The translations appearing in this text are mine. *Tr.*

[5]The answers of Ch'I-Po to the Yellow Emperor are quoted in Dr. Choain, *Voie Rationelle de la Medecine Chinoise*, p. 455. For the original, see *Yellow Emperor's Classic of Internal Medicine*, p.133.

A popular saying tells us that it is good to "have a heart of gold." Gold is pure, invulnerable, immutable. The heart of gold is that of the Sage whose perpetual movement comes from the Wisdom which Is.

But gold is also the symbol of life: the Incas worshipped the sun which is the center of our planetary system, the alchemists seek the philosopher's stone which transmutes all into gold, and the kabbalists place Tiphareth (the 6th Sephira) in the center of the Tree on the Pillar of Balance, this being the Sephira of the sun and of gold.

In a scene representing the Judgment after Death, an Egyptian papyrus (Papyrus An XVII, 39) depicts a scale: on one of its trays rests the heart of the deceased, on the other the feather of Maat, goddess of Justice. To be cleared by the divine tribunal, it is necessary for "the heart to be as light as a feather."

No sort of excess must weigh down the heart; all passions checked (but not repressed) bring balance.

Enel reminds us that the ancient teachings acknowledged the existence of two organs, each one called Heart. One was written AB and the other HATI.[6] AB symbolized *intelligence*: "I understand through my heart."[7] HATI connects the spirit to matter and symbolizes the *passions* (the Na-Hash of the Hebrew kabbalists): "I rule through my heart."

Applied to the psychology of the organs in Chinese thought, we see that AB = psychic energy = the heart is a treasury organ. HATI = vital energy = the heart is a husband organ. According to the state of the organ function in connection with the heart, we can go a long way toward understanding the significance of this organ in relation to Being.

---

[6]*La Langue Sacrée*, p. xxii.

[7]Dr. Niboyet says in his *Essai sur l'Acupuncture Chinoise Pratique*, p. 20, "The heart meridian has a nourishing influence upon the brain, and so an influence upon intelligence." The translation is mine. *Tr.*

Tarot: 21st major arcanum, the World

If the Heart is the reflection of life by way of its incessant circulatory movement, the 21st arcanum corresponds to it perfectly; in the laurel wreath we find the very symbol of life and victory. This is a solar plant, and through its composition in the form of a crown, it symbolizes life which circulates unceasingly. In the four elements (fire, earth, air, water) at the four corners of the card, we find the symbol of balance; and in the young androgynous figure in the center of the wreath we have the symbol of the sun, creator of life. Oswald Wirth describes it in this way:

> She is the corporal soul of the universe, the Vestal Virgin of the hearth of life whose fire burns in every person.[8] This role explains the two wands which the sulphureous maiden holds in her left hand. They have round knobs at the end, of which one is red and the other blue. With the first, fiery energies are picked up, which will be associated with the life-giving fire which would die out if it were not constantly revived by the breath of air which the blue knob attracts. When the energies are picked up they are passed with the right hand to the red veil that she is holding.[9]

To look at this symbolism further, we find that a red wand = heart, husband organ; the blue wand = lungs, wife organ; and the right hand on the veil = intestines, factory

---

[8]This young girl reappears on the 17th arcanum, which is that of PHE (p and f), which corresponds to the intestines, a reflection of sensitivity.

[9]Oswald Wirth, *The Tarot of the Magicians* (York Beach, Maine: Samuel Weiser, 1985), p. 150. Originally published in 1927 in French under the title *Les Tarots des Imagiers du Moyene Age*. The tarot images used in this book are from the Wirth tarot deck published by U. S. Games, Stamford, CT. The deck is also available from Samuel Weiser, Inc.

organ. We are here in the midst of psychic energy, the Egyptian AB which symbolizes the intelligence of things.

The young girl holds two rods: In High Magic wands gathered in one hand signify an action simultaneously opposed and transmitted.[10] In magic as well as in psychic forces to be collected, everyone knows how indispensible is the inner balance of Being. A profound meditation on this arcanum will lead us to personal discoveries upon the heart, the world, and the concept of balance.

Form of the Horizontal Bars on the *t*

The size and the direction of the horizontal bars of the *t* give us the physical functioning, good or bad, of the heart organ function, and the degree of feeling, sensitivity, the intelligence of the writer's heart regarding others and life.

T bars irregularly placed, even omitted, are indicative of a heart which beats unevenly, stops and then starts again. It is indicative of a sensitivity subject to the vicissitudes of life which overwhelm the psychic state and disturb the equilibrium. It is passion which shoots up like an arrow, or plunges straight down, endangering the safety of those in its path.

A bar which extends abnormally, either to the right or to the left, over neighboring letters, does not signify a heart that beats too much: there is a just proportion in all things. It shows a heart which is solid and stalwart, which likes to protect and shelter those around it under a maternal wing — with perhaps a little too much zeal. If this person is good and the spleen-pancreas *q* (formation of ideas) functions well, then joy is the byword. But beware of this individual's "passion" for protecting.

---

[10]*The Tarot of the Magicians*, p. 150.

The horizontal bar of this example *t* seems to want to set out to conquer. The person is ambitious — perhaps joyous, but the joy is artificial, for serence and balanced joy does not advertise itself.

The heart as organ is subjected to excesses of feeling provoked by fatigue and an overload of tension.

The second example shows that the bar descends; to do battle against those who are socially inferior doesn't help matters. The irritability of this writer is marked and is a cause of heart palpitations.

If we consider the symbol of the Egyptian scale, we notice that this scale has its right platform in the lower position: psychic energy is misdirected and the intelligence is that of HATI, which attaches the spirit to matter in its least evolved sense.

The stubborn headstrong person crosses the *t*'s twice; that is to say, he or she attaches it to the ground once and crosses it again on top, this time in the standard manner, as shown in our third example.

This writer controls feelings to the point of holding sensitivity on a leash (see the *p*'s which relate to sensitivity). This state is comparable to that of a scale (of the kind used in pharmacies) whose platform cannot function because the axis is locked in position. The qualities of the heart are therefore willfully constrained; to control emotions is a virtue, but to repress them is a dangerous game.

This bar which floats in the air (our fourth example) places the writer between two tendencies: to have a heart or to be without one. Hesitant are the intentions which emanate from the heart, for their realization involves attaching the bar to the stem. Feelings float according to the whim of the passions that move them, as the wind moves a weathervane or lifts a leaf. The intelligence has trouble finding its realization.

The heart as organ is submitted to an unsatisfying rhythm/rate and protests by way of heart attacks. If the lungs (*h*) do not restore balance in the heart's place by breathing deeply (*h* well delineated), the heart suffers not only from its own poor condition, but also from the insufficient output of its wife. As it is, tubercular people are obliged to spend long hours resting so as to manage their hearts.

The bar in the fifth example greatly exceeds the norm and is too large for its vertical stem, anything attached to either end of it would topple it. It is characteristic of excessive feeling. The heart no longer acts in its capacity as a treasury organ, but rather as a factory organ, due to its activity (length of bar). It is psychic energy which is overcharged, displaced; it lacks balance and stability. As for the vital energy, it is strong but subject to unpleasant surprises, for its unstable equilibrium could fall apart. One must remember that the heart is never a factory organ. Psychologically speaking, this is a type of person who protects everyone without discrimination, due to an exaggerated AB.

The Intestines

Function:	The large intestine is a yang factory organ. (yin treasury organ = the lungs). The large intestine is wife (its husband = the small intestine). The small intestine is a yang factory organ. (yin treasury organ = the heart). The small intestine is a husband organ (its wife = the large intestine).
Latin letter:	In graphology we will study the intestines in general: *p* and *f*.
Hebrew letter: ב	PE. The symbolic image is of the human mouth, whose most beautiful attribute it depicts — that of expressing our thoughts. Its particular expression is emphasis. It controls speech and all that relates to it.[11] Essential action.
Egyptian hieroglyph:	It represents a slug, symbol of creeping and undulatory movement.
Tarot:	17th major arcanum, the Star.

Role of the Intestines

The two intestines are the kinetic organs of the process of material absorption. In Chinese medicine, they are both yang

---

[11]Speech viewed as expression of the Creative Logos corresponds to *r*, RESH; since there are no correspondences in Chinese medicine, this letter will not be considered in this study.

factory organs. On the one hand, they absorb the outer environment and create a choice whereby the best elements are fed into the blood's circulation; and on the other, they eliminate what is unnecessary. Ch'I-Po told the Yellow Emperor that, "the small intestines are like the officials who are trusted with riches, and they create changes of the physical substance; . . . the lower intestines are like the officials who propagate the Right Way of Living, and they generate evolution and change."[12]

Psychology

The convolutions of the intestines are similar to those of the brain. The digestive evolution is parallel to that of the nervous system. For example, many students taking exams often empty the brain of accumulated knowledge, along with the intestines! The large intestine, as Minister of Transportation sweeps everything away. How? Through sensitivity. The seat of *sensitivity* is in the intestines. They vibrate, they move unceasingly; in cases of intense feelings their activity affects the heart (the treasury organ of the small intestines). How many patients think they have heart trouble when in fact they have an intestinal disorder because of unchecked sensitivity.

♦ The small intestine works with psychic energy.

♦ The large intestine works with vital energy.

These two treasury organs play a very large role in our general health. It has been said that, the small intestine adds to the dead nutrients from the stomach an element of life absolutely unique to each individual. Laboratory research conducted on this point has led to the discovery that the duodenum breaks apart the large molecules of albumin and creates small molecules of albumin absolutely unique to the tissues

---

[12]See the *Yellow Emperor*, p. 133.

and blood of each individual; molecules formed of atoms in perpetual motion.[13] As above, so below; vital energy and psychic energy are related in the working of these two organ-functions.

In another way, the intestines symbolize the Minister of Finance. In fact, the large intestine eliminates the wastes sorted out by the small intestine; it either eliminates or holds on to them. Accordingly, those who mismanage finances through frivolous spending or excessive thrift have maladjusted intestines; it is rare not to find constipation in misers. And by misers I mean those who want to save for themselves, people who collect things, be it strings, or tin cans; people who want to hold onto emotional property and will not yield any part of it. No matter what we are sensitive about, it will show in the intestines.

Tarot: 17th major arcanum, the Star

Astrologers place the intestines in the sign of Virgo and it is with the Virgin of the Star that the PE is associated in the tarot. This card is the symbol of a continuous task carried out with calm, harmony and balance.

The young girl on this card is an integral part of her natural surroundings; water flows from two vessels, the factory is calm and does not cease its work. Above her are eight stars, this number is that of balance (4 + 4), of good management. It corresponds to HETH, which represents the Lungs (*h*), treasury organs of the large intestine. And we know that any disorder provoked by excessive sensitivity, with repercussions on the heart, can only be balanced through the lungs and the breath.

---

[13]Soulié de Morant, *Acupuncture Chinoise* (Paris: Editions Maldine, 1972), p. 283.

This 17th arcanum is "the soul joining matter and spirit." Without the intestines, matter—being unliberated—would not allow the spirit to evolve; and without the humus of the earth, how could the spirit resume its form?

Form of the *p* and the *f*

These two letters need to be examined in association as much as possible.

The *p* in our first example is marked by a definite enclosure and is typical of those who like to economize, who like to hang on or hoard.

Medically speaking, constipation is a fact. This *f* in our second example is from the same text. Its ink-filled lower loop confirms an intestinal sluggishness due to a desire to hoard.

The *p* in our third example is very heavily traced in the lower portion, and forms a path that looks like a highway; money flows rapidly, while vital energy, strong and without any detours, feeds the writer. The flow of speech is broad, abundant and emphatic.

Our fourth example shows a LAMED *l* adds itself to the PHE; this denotes people who profess (PE = speech) self-sacrifice and devotion (LAMED = sacrifice). They also experience a need for expansion (LAMED = the extended arm) through speech. This relieves them and allows them to maintain balance. The sensitivity they feel is more imagined than real. It is often called sentimentality.

The LAMED here (added to the *p*) is doubled at the bottom by an unnecessary loop. This indicates a case of chronic constipation. The writer tries to clear the convolutions of the brain (analogous to the intestines) through a stream of words as if, by emptying one, he could avoid the fullness of the other. Sensitivity is intense, misguided, and occasions psychological problems. In the same text, here is how the *f*s are constructed:

The *f* shows the Egyptian slug. In the deeper, more intimate part (the lower loop) this person is attached to the past (inclined to the left). This unconscious link to the "navel" of the Mother (initiatory meaning of the Egyptian PE[14]) is an

---

[14]*La Langue Sacrée*, p. 78.

added reason for the writer, who feels himself heavy and entrapped by matter, to free himself through speech. His psychic energy resents this struggle; it is deficient.

This extremely simplified *f* is reduced to the bare essentials and represents a lively, fine, and keen sensitivity. The sentences are pointed, almost trenchant, there is no verbiage and the *p* presents the same form.

The Bladder

Function:	The bladder is a yang factory organ (its yin treasury organ is the kidneys). The bladder is husband (its wife is the triple heater).
Latin letter:	*n*
Hebrew letter: ב	NUN. Image of the materialized or conceptualized Being: a sign of individual and corporeal existence.
Egyptian hieroglyph: 〰	Passivity, negation relative to the evolutionary-involutionary movement of BETH. It is passivity as the complementary return of action.
Tarot:	14th major arcanum, Temperance.

Role of the Bladder

The bladder is a sac that fills and empties according to the rhythm imposed by its treasury organ, the kidneys. Its role is to eliminate, to evacuate the liquid for which the inner environment has no need. Through this eliminatory action, this factory-function organ regulates the equilibrium of the nervous system.

Soulié de Morant said that: the bladder is the Minister of the Capitol of the Valleys. And Ch'I-Po told the Yellow Emperor that the bladder is like the local Magistrate who contains the flooding and regulates evaporation (Regulatory Control and Repairs).[15]

Psychology

Elimination is subordinate to the will which is itself directed by the cerebral system.[16] It is therefore the result of a higher process.

Everyone can observe that the kidneys/bladder rhythm deteriorates or is deficient during two stages of life — infancy and old age. Why is this? Using the Chinese point of view, we would say that it is during these two stages that circulation-sexuality is not fully active. This function is connected to the cerebral system, and is deregulated through its deficient activity. When the bladder is a poorly directed factory, it can only eliminate in a haphazard fashion.

Psychologically speaking, the baby does not control its cerebral system, nor the nerves which correspond to it, and so there is bed-wetting until the will and decision come into play. Similarly, the elderly person who is tired of life lets go of the kidneys, the masters of the nerves and will, and the saturated bladder no longer controls itself. It is rare to see a

---

[15]See the *Yellow Emperor*, p. 133.
[16]The cerebral system consists of kidneys, bladder and circulation-sexuality.

spry elderly person with urinary incontinence, for cerebral consciousness can remain active until physical death.

Psychic energy relates to the cerebral system as we will discuss in chapter 5. The bladder plays its role as a regulator through its eliminatory function: it therefore acts upon the psychic equilibrium of the individual. In the words of Niboyet: "The bladder, in addition to its role as a reservoir, apparently has an excitatory and regulatory action on the kidneys, and also it would seem, on the psyche."[17]

Tarot: 14th major arcanum, Temperance

This tarot card shows a young woman, standing, holding two urns, one in gold (the Sun) and the other in silver (the Moon). What has been collected in the silver urn (kidney = yin = psyche and concentration) flows into the golden urn (bladder = yang = action), where condensation takes place in the interest of physical maintenance. This card is the symbol of continuity, of unending rhythm, and also of psychic balance (water).

When the major arcana of the tarot are placed in two rows, the 9th arcanum, the Hermit, becomes the companion of Temperance: and we already know that the Hermit corresponds to the kidneys and Temperance to the bladder.

Form of the *n*

$$n$$

This letter, which appears to be an *n*, is in fact an *r*. The handwriting in the text where it appears is small, secretive,

---

[17]Niboyet, *Essai sur l'Acupuncture Chinoise Pratique*, p. 37. The translation is mine. *Tr.*

and repressed. We can say that speech (RESH) plays the role
of the bladder: it evacuates only that of which it wants to be
rid.

ᘒ

The *n* with a swollen inner pocket is typical of a bladder
in pain—difficulty in elimination with a tendency toward
inflammation. The vessel does not want to fulfill its function
anymore, and so it hinders the physical maintenance through
deficient psychic energy. This *n* has the form of the astrological sign of the Lion. Leo, as it happens, is a fire sign, and, of
course, inflammation of the bladder also burns.

ᘯ

This *n* ends abruptly with a resolute stroke and anchors
itself into the baseline instead of extending itself to the following letter. The nervous tension of this bladder meridian is
intense. This man wants his desires to be catered to and
unquestionably carried out.

The psychic balance is thus troubled by a rigid will that
does not permit the bladder to function in its role as regulator. Its eliminatory capabilities are weak and it easily
becomes inflammed or obstructed.

ᘰ

This tiny little *n* turns back into itself; it is smaller than
the other letters in the text. The form and size indicate that
the bladder meridian is a Minister of the Rivers that does
nothing, is introverted, and gives as little as possible (urina-
tion is infrequent at only three times a day).

ᘱ

The *n* in this sample begins by rising upward from the
baseline to form a loop, it goes to the left—toward the past—

forms a figure 8 and from there proceeds up and to the right; as it descends it takes on the shape of an *i*. The bladder meridian here is stressed by latent and chronic problems (the figure 8 and its endless circumvolutions and that it is interlaced into the letter) that have something to do with the father (*i*) and with men (*n*). Bitterness has inflamed this bladder (figure 8), it is covered with cysts.

This woman was abandoned, since birth, by her father, and this circumstance has programmed her attitude (the bladder) toward life and men.

n

All of the *n*'s take on the shape of the Ram, symbol for the fire sign Aries. This fire and passion affects the nervous tension, causing it to be irregular and therefore detrimental to the overall psychological balance. It starts but does not finish anything. The midpart of the letter is also looped and filled in with ink; anger obstructs this bladder.

The Kidneys

Function:	The kidneys are yin treasury organs (the yang factory organ is the bladder).
	The kidneys are husband (the wife is circulation-sexuality).
Latin letter:	For the left kidney it is *v*.
Hebrew letter:	VAU. Represents the ear and becomes the symbol of sound, noise, the wind.[18]

---

[18]VAU is also connected to the triple heater in its other representation. See page 71.

Egyptian hieroglyph:	Understanding of that which is Self and that which is not Self.
	The hieroglyph is a chick, which relates to the microcosm.[19]

Tarot: Left Kidney, 6th major arcanum, the Lovers.

Latin
letters: Each kidney has a specific letter which corresponds to it. For the right kidney it is the vertical bar of *t*. TETH.

Hebrew
letter: TETH. Symbolic image is the shield; resistance
and protection.

Egyptian
hieroglyph: Symbolizes connection, the action of unifying,
of possessing things.

Tarot: Right Kidney, 9th major arcanum, the Hermit.

The Role of the Kidney

The kidney belongs to a world that does not interact with the outside. It is a yin organ-function whose work is completely inward. It can be compared to a gate that functions to balance, stabilize, concentrate and maintain an integrity of the form whose structure has been provided by the spleen-pancreas. The kidney is the balance of the form. For this work, the nerves must come into play: in Chinese medicine the kidneys are called "the masters of the nerves."

---

[19]The spiral, which is essentially macrocosmic, applies to the triple heater.

The general shape of the kidney corresponds to that of the ear, which reminds us that this organ also acts as a barrier in filtering or limiting sounds and thus balancing the vibrations that strike it. This led Nei-Ching to say: "The ear is the mouth of the kidney."

How often elderly people become deaf! A deficiency in this organ is the warning that alerts us to a disfunction of the kidneys which will express itself in later life through problems with the kidney-bladder relationship.

Soulié de Morant said that the kidneys are the Ministers who produce robustness and vital energy. They accumulate decisiveness, cleverness, sexual energy. And Ch'I-Po told the Yellow Emperor that the kidneys are like the officials who carry out their work energetically, and who excel by their competence and skill (the craftsmen and manufacturers).[20]

Psychology

The kidney is a treasury organ: it concentrates, decides, wants. It acts upon decision. It also acts upon physical, moral and psychic force and robustness. There is a French expression, "avoir les reins solides" (literally, to have strong kidneys, to have strong resources), which is applied to those who have all of these qualities.

Physically, the kidneys concentrate: the spiritual reflection of this is mental concentration whose fruit is psychic equilibrium. But it must be kept in mind that kidneys that are in bad shape can produce the opposite effect, namely fear. Remember, for example, that children in the grips of great fear or uncontrollable laughter (both the result of an uncontrolled will) often "pee in their pants."

---

[20]See the *Yellow Emperor*, p. 133.

We say that, "he was so scared his hair stood on end," and Soulié de Morant said that the kidneys flower in the hair. Fear relates to hair and the kidneys. The kidneys are also related to the hair in Chinese medicine. And we know that the hair covers the skull in which is located the mental system whose treasury organ is the kidneys.

In the same vein, the biblical story of Samson illustrates a similar concept. He was a warrior of extraordinary strength (robustness comes from the kidneys) who had long hair (the kidneys flower in the hair). Delilah, a treacherous woman (organ-function = circulation-sexuality, wife of the kidneys) cut off his hair, which is how Samson lost his power.

During menopause, around age 50, the circulation-sexuality system becomes a problem for its spouse the kidneys because of the change of rhythm. Our hair turns gray or white and many women decide to dye it. This brings on certain problems, both physical and those related to psychic balance, for the nerves are in a frayed state (nerves being masters of the kidneys).

Because of their correspondence with the ears, the kidneys have a direct relationship to music. It is well known that music calms the nerves: and as it happens, the nerves are master of the kidneys. Music calms the nerves, and contributes to the proper functioning of the kidneys when the ear is exposed to certain types of classical music (such as the fugues and cantatas of Bach). Music can also excite and stimulate the nerves by vibrating sexual energy through the mental system (certain passages of Tristan and Yseult), or overexcite them with jazz, and even bring them to the point of hysteria with certain pieces of music (rock and roll) which play exclusively on circulation-sexuality, the spouse of the kidneys.

Tarot for Left Kidney: 6th major arcanum, the Lovers; *v*

The Lovers represents the one who must choose in order to orient himself (kidney = decision).

Tarot for Right Kidney: 9th major arcanum, the Hermit; *t* (vertical bar)

The Hermit is one who works in depth, going into the inner life of things, and does so in silence. Without concentration, the Hermit could not work fruitfully. He accumulates energy, safe from any infiltration (the kidneys being a form of barrier). He lives in an austere and balanced psychic environment (a reflection of the kidneys). The left kidney is the husband organ of the wife ear.

In the tarot the will is described by three arcana:

◆ the Emperor (*d*, gall bladder) wills in an imperative fashion;

◆ the Pope (*e*, circulation-sexuality) emanates a gentle and patient will;

◆ the Lovers (*v*, kidneys) desires in a state of meditation and profound affection.

In the Lovers' decision, the kidneys play the initiatory role of the will.

Form of the *v* (left kidney) and *t* (right kidney)

We will later on consider the *v* as corresponding to the triple heater which will only reinforce the correspondences between this letter and the will.

Only the form of the vertical bar of the *t* is to be examined for the right kidney (the horizontal bar relates to the heart).

This strongly drawn *t* presents the form of a pocket: the kidney in this case is no longer playing the role of a filter but that of a reservoir like the bladder. This represents an excess of concentration by the kidneys (the excess being indicated by the violence of the line, the concentration by the formation of a pocket). This excessive concentration does not allow sufficient drainage toward the bladder.

Through an excess of will, the woman who writes in this way has paralyzed her cerebral system. This means that the mental sexuality is strong but that its realization is blocked. In the same text the *v*'s were like so:

Very open and expansive: there is more letting go than concentration!

We can conclude that if the right kidney, is too closed, and in contrast the left kidney is too open, then there is a lack of balance in mental sexuality.

Psychic balance is not well-developed and the nerves are subjected to the extremes of an iron will and letting go. This condition can certainly bring little joy to their owner for too many things "get on her nerves." When this happens, she says that she covers her ears to keep from going mad.

If we apply the idea of will and decision to the 6th arcanum, we would say that the writer is "manic-depressive."

Either she concentrates too much, as her *t*'s indicate, or, according to her *v*'s, she lets herself go too much.

This *t* floating above the base line indicates a poor functioning of the right kidney. Instead of resting on the line, the letter rises like a kite. The will is susceptible to influence in its decisions and we can suppose that this individual has trouble concentrating.

However, it also indicates that the writer has a tendency to do without material things in order to acquire spiritual values; material values are represented by the part located between the line and the bottom of the letter, the part which is missing. The spiritual values are also indicated by the cross form of this letter which was clearly and precisely drawn.

As for the *v*'s, they are like this — clear, small and precise, resting on the line. Since this handwriting is that of a spiritually evolved person, the *v* functions in a macrocosmic rather than microcosmic way, we would conclude that the deficiency noted in the right kidney has not been realized physically; but it would be a vulnerable spot in the event of an illness or shock. Everything is taking place on the level of the psyche, where balance is good (neatness and precision in the tracing of the two letters).

This is the *v* of a person who wants to control everything: materially, spiritually, and sexually; in every case she decides: "I'm in charge." We see that it takes the form of the zodiacal sign of the Ram (Aries) which is that of the leader.

In the same handwriting, here is the form of the *t*. It is a *b* folded over itself, which brings us back to the concept of concentration, of decision-making, of the will even in the context of evolution since BETH is a very spiritual letter. But this activity could be to the detriment of the kidney because the *t* looks like a knot.

This *t* has the form of an *l*. Instead of concentrating, this kidney gives (LAMED = expansion).

As for the *v*, it becomes an *m* throughout the text. The *m* is the MEM, Death, and the Mother. At the same time, the direction of this handwriting is inclined toward the left, and presents an aspect of isolation and nervosity. This case of nervous imbalance and fear could result in a degeneration of the kidneys and that could affect the female organs (womb = MEM) and also severely disturb circulation-sexuality (spouse of the kidneys); that, psychologically, this fear could become so severe as to predispose her to a terminal illness (MEM = death) and psychically, that an imbalance causes a great deal of indecision.

And again, this imbalance has serious repercussions on the circulation-sexuality meridian; it is often referred to as Master of the Heart for it provides it with protective ramparts. When circulation-sexuality gives out, so does the heart. This woman was said to have died of a broken heart when actually the kidneys were at fault.

Circulation-Sexuality

Function: Circulation-sexuality is a yin treasury organ (its yang factory organ is the triple heater). Circulation-sexuality is wife (the husband is the kidneys).
This meridian does not correspond to an organ, but rather to a function. It has another name, which is Master of the Heart.

Latin
letters: *j*, Positive Masculine, creative principle.

Hebrew
letter: YOD, Image of the manifested principle. It is a sign of spiritual duration, of the infinity of time, and of all the ideas which relate to it.

Egyptian
hieroglyph: Manifestation replaces the Principle.
Self-realization as bearer of the divine spark.

Tarot: *j*, 10th major arcanum, the Wheel of Fortune.

Latin
letter: *e*, Negative Fertilized Feminine Principle.

Hebrew
letter: HE. It is the connection between spirit, soul and body, or the Neschamah, Ruach and Nephesch of the Hebrew Kabbalah. It symbolizes the life of the Being. Taken by itself, it is inanimate and passive, it is triggered by the life

principle, YOD, and it furnishes it with the necessary elements for its vital manifestations.

Egyptian
hieroglyph:

A cord twisted into three loops, which represent the Unity of the three levels—it corresponds to the soul. By way of the links on the chain the dual involutionary-evolutionary current circulates; on the one hand it transmits the concepts of reason formed by the will and manifested as action, and on the other hand, it carries toward reason the impressions of external life as received by the senses.

Tarot: *e*, 5th major arcanum, the Pope.

Latin
letter: *z*

Hebrew
letter:

ZAYIN. Symbolic image: the cycle of the human being, the end toward which we tend.

Egyptian
hieroglyph:

A serpent in movement. This continual exchange creates the cycle of life that is eternity symbolized by ZAYIN, the serpent in movement, swiftness, the journey, all that is distant.[21]

Tarot: *z*, 18th major arcanum, the Moon.

---

[21]"All letters expressive of the *z* sound within the various alphabets seem to have the Egyptian serpent as their origin." Enel, *La Langue Sacrée*, p. 60. The translation is mine. *Tr.*

Role of Circulation-Sexuality

Strictly speaking, we are dealing here not with a physical organ, but with a function described by Chinese medicine. It is active on three levels — the Cerebral, the Physical, and the Spiritual.

The Cerebral: Circulation-sexuality is wife of the kidneys within the cerebral system.[22] It is from the mind that all ideas, all directives emerge. We are on the level of mental sexuality from which originates all reasoning. It is this conception of sexuality that puts the physical plane into gear.

The Physical: The active creative masculine force united with the fertilized female force is the physical materialization of circulation-sexuality as conceived by the mind. On the physical level, the role of this Chinese function is twofold: first, it reproduces, as we have said (sexuality), and second, it compensates this outflow by bringing back from the periphery to the center the flow of blood which the heart had sent into the arteries and veins (circulation). Its second name — Master of the Heart — is related to this particular role.

The Spiritual: This function symbolizes the life of the Being, Bearer of the Divine Spark, from its conception to its dissolution. Like the serpent in movement, it can find itself getting bogged down in matter[23] through an involutionary cycle, or else, come to bloom through an evolutionary spiritual ascent.[24]

---

[22]See chapter 4.

[23]According to Enel in *La Langue Sacrée* (p. 206), "In general, the Egyptian goddesses had as a definite article the hieroglyph for serpent, which alludes to the idea that it is by way of the feminine principle that evil is manifested, that is to say, attachment to matter." The translation is mine. *Tr.*

[24]Again, in *La Langue Sacrée* (p. 206) Enel tells us, "An Egyptian goddess has a name where TZADDI was written next to the sign for the tongue of fire and evolution above matter." The translation is mine. *Tr.*

Soulié de Morant said that the Master of the Heart is the Minister of Unions, the Mother of the Blood and of yin. As Ch'I-Po told the Yellow Emperor that the Master of the Heart is the official who guides the subjects in their joys and pleasures.[25]

Psychology

It is breathing that gives us the air so necessary for physical life: it represents not the vital cause but the means for life. We all have our own particular breathing and we use it according to our temperament and needs. By analogy, the circulation-sexuality function that exists in all living beings is differently directed in each of us.

Mentally, the sexual concept comes into play to provide shape to the quality of reasoning. A healthy sexual intelligence acts upon the psyche and the physical body so that the female reproductive organs and the masculine sexual organs function in a harmonious rhythm. An unhealthy mental sexual concept leads to a psychic imbalance, with a tendency towards abnormality, perversion, or sexual atrophy.[26]

Western education frequently distorts this Chinese function from childhood onward for various religious, moral, or social reasons which are poorly explained or understood. Freud, in his own way, often said that European sexual eduction was based on an erroneous foundation and that was why there were so many people who had a deformed mental sexuality and who were living with a serious imbalance.

---

[25]See the *Yellow Emperor*, p. 133.

[26]In this case, study the *c*'s (CAPH), for the Egyptian symbolism is described by Enel as the medium where the mixture of the forces that create material manifestation take place.

Tarot: 10th major arcanum, the Wheel of Fortune; *j*

The wheel is an image of life that is forever creating, circulating like an electrical current whose concentric circles always return to the hub of the wheel. From the lunar bark, the female principle of fecundity, rise two snakes, symbols of the positive and the negative. The wheel carries Herm-Anubis and a Typhonian creature symbolizing the movement of the constructive and destructive energies, both of which create and stimulate life. The sphinx that surmounts the wheel corresponds to the four elements — earth and water from the Moon (sexuality), fire and air from the Sun (circulation).

Tarot: 5th major arcanum, the Pope; *e*

The Pope corresponds to the fire of Aries (the Ram), which is that of intelligence. Agni descended from the sky in order to ignite himself at the center of the swastika cross when the rites were enacted. In this arcanum we see that the old man who, by the wisdom of his reasoning (circulation-sexuality), knows how to balance psychic energy, and so lead to knowledge, the fruit of wisdom.

Tarot: 18th major arcanum, the Moon; *z*

 Under the lunar influence, this card shows that the imagination goes into operation and precedes reason, which in turn induces false mental theories. In divination, this card warns of dangers created by inconsistent or false mental concepts. By the symbolism of the two flesh-colored towers crowned with gold, it also shows that intelligent Beings who are able to act with discernment, by virtue of mental and sexual balance, are not influenced by the mirages of the Moon.

These two towers also symbolize the two Pillars of the Temple — between which the Initiated can stand erect because they have succeeded in liberating themselves from material attachment. The crowns of gold symbolize the wisdom attained.

Form of the *j*, *e*, and *z*

To understand the rhythm of this Chinese function within each individual — a function far removed from our Western concepts, but yet a very profound one — we should examine the *j*, *e*, and *z* together.

In a woman's handwriting the *j*'s are normal, such as in our first example. The YOD is a sign of spiritual duration and of the ideas which relate to it. It is the Ego, Bearer of the Divine Spark. Here it has not been obstructed.

In our second example, we see the *e*'s are filled in. The feminine principle has not been fertilized; it has not received the stimulus of the YOD, or has not mentally realized it. Here psychic energy will encounter an obstacle to its balance, and in particular to its ascent. Physically, the reproductive organs are not in good condition (especially the ovaries).

$$3$$

The z's are barely drawn (third example), the form is there but it is incomplete. There is no attachment to matter (lower loop sketchy), but we would have to suppose that the cosmic egg is in a latent state only (unfinished letter). Intelligence has not recognized sexuality and prefers to ignore the subject.

In this particular person, the circulation-sexuality function is not operating harmoniously. The deficiency will show on the mental level — mental sexuality is based on false reasoning. On a physical level, we may find a problem with the female sexual organs, a repercussion of the mental blockage. The blood circulation is defective. On the spiritual level we see that the evolutive current is blocked, but this condition is not definitive; it is a temporary halt.

$$T$$

In another case, the j is capped by a horizontal line, as if in an effort to prevent the letter, and what it represents, from rising higher. We are dealing here with a mental concept that refuses to accord sexuality its spiritual aspect.

If with a j of this sort, and if the e's are not blocked, the j is often the sign of an inferiority complex arising from the person's fears over the unknown consequences of spiritual evolution. Symbolically, the writer prefers a low ceiling which she can see to a clear sky of which she knows nothing. However, if the e's are filled in, this indicates a disruption of the circulation-sexuality function on all levels.

The Triple Heater

Function:
The triple heater (or three heaters) is a yang factory organ (its treasury is circulation-sexuality). The triple heater is wife (its husband is the bladder). It does not correspond to an organ but to a function.

Latin letter: *v*

Hebrew letter:

VAU represents the most ineffable and profound mystery, the image of the point of convergence or of divergence of being and nothingness. It is the universal sign of transmutation, the sign that effects the passage from one nature to another; communicating on the one side with the sign of light and of the spiritual sense which is the elevated VAU, and crossing over and connecting with the shadowy side AYIN, or the material sense which is the debased VAU. And so VAU has two interpretations: one is microcosmic as it relates to the yang that is distributed throughout the meridians and that is associated with the left kidney, and the other is macrocosmic as it relates to the triple heater — which is sometimes referred to as the father of yang.

Egyptian hieroglyph:

A macrocosmic spiral.[27] This represents the vortex of cosmic forces which were set in motion by the creator to accomplish the work

---

[27]The image of the chick, which is microcosmic, relates to the left kidney.

of differentiation of matter and of all the manifestations of life in the universe. The action of
these forces created definite combinations of
the four elements (air, water, earth, fire) all of
which emerged from the same Mother. This
hieroglyph is essentially macrocosmic.

Tarot: 6th major arcanum, the Lovers.

Role of the Triple Heater

On the physical plane, the triple heater maintains a constant
body temperature regardless of the ambient temperature. It
circulates the energy in the canals and affects the major respiratory, digestive, and genito-urinary functions.

Soulié de Morant said that the triple heater is the Minister of the Irrigation and Drainage Canals, the storehouse of
inner purity, the Father of energy and yang. Ch'I-Po told the
Yellow Emperor that the triple heater is like the officials who
design the blueprints of the canals and locks and who create
channels (the plan)."[28]

This function operates not on one, but on three levels:
its action is threefold. It is physical, affective, spiritual.

Fabre d'Olivet once said that VAU corresponds to the
Chinese radicals which express all of the ideas of fire, life,
heat, action, Being.

It is through the triple heater that we are in contact with
cosmic vibrations. It is the antenna that receives the emitted
energy and transmits it throughout the organism by way of
the gall bladder, which serves as its reflector: the microcosm
is like the macrocosm.

---

[28]See the *Yellow Emperor*, p. 133.

Psychology

The triple heater gives energy, vivacity, and enthusiasm. It gives that taste for life which is without any neurotic overtones. It is comparable to sunshine and its benefits: when it shines the nerve's energy are strong. However, when the triple heater malfunctions life feels bland and monotonous like an overcast day. Sorrow and depression, unless there is a change, inevitably follow.

The triple heater is our contact with the Cosmos that is infinite in its evolutive possibilities and resources of psychic energy.

Tarot: 6th major arcanum, the Lovers

 This corresponds to the 6th sephira of the Kabbalah, Tiphareth, whose emblem is the seal of Solomon, and is composed of two interpenetrating triangles. It alludes to the union of the human soul and the divine spirit, a fire sign, a current that comes from the Cosmos. It is the Star of the macrocosm, sign of the supreme magical power obtained by the individual. Now, 6 and 6 by 3 bring us back to the Trinity.[29] The Three Heaters are a Triple unity.

This arcanum already appeared in correspondence with the left kidney. Like the letter VAU, which is also associated with the left kidney, the Lovers offers more than one potential path. In the words of Oswald Wirth:

> The Lovers hesitate, urged (like Hercules) by an austere queen who only promises moral satisfaction and by a bacchante, the provider of easy pleasures.[30]

---

[29]By so-called theosophic addition: $6 + 6 = 12$, $12 = 1 + 2 = 3$.
[30]*The Tarot of the Magicians*, p. 85.

and further:

> So arcana 6 as a whole illustrates the mechanism of
> the voluntary act of the sentient person portrayed
> by the Lover who is 'L'Homme de Désir' (Desiring
> Man) of Saint-Martin. This personality receives the
> impressions of the physical world thanks to his sen-
> sitivity (the green colour of his costume), then he
> reacts (red colour, propulsion). Now as it is not a
> matter of unconscious or automatic acts, called
> reflex, there is deliberation, choice before the
> releasing of the action is decided upon.[31]

Form of the *v*

Keep in mind the fact that the triple heater sends the cosmic
energy to the gall bladder. The VAU, in the sense of a current
of cosmic energy, must be studied only in the handwriting of
those who are evolved or able to be receptive, in which case
we must also study the form of the *d*'s, the gall bladder.

This is the *v* of someone who closes himself off from the
yang sun and who is too self-involved. By the same token, he
cuts himself off from the influx of cosmic energy and the
result is a VAU that attaches itself in its decay to the shadowy
AYIN. AYIN corresponds to the letter *o*, and we can see that
this *v* approaches its form. It is the Tower of the Tarot, the
me of the egotist.

It is interesting to note, too, that if the v takes on completely the form of the *o* (by being closed) it is to be inter-
preted in the sense of the Tower struck by lightning, that is,
physical death. In a handwriting that presents this feature,

---

[31]*The Tarot of the Magicians*, p. 86.

physical death. In a handwriting that presents this feature, death is of greater concern than life (*o* = death, and *v* = the fire of life). I have often observed that the *m*'s (MEM = the Mother, and death) gave a clue to the origin of many disturbances that can be occasioned by the mystery that shrouds this matter, disturbances that often reach the point of a great imbalance (the *t* bars are then also influenced).

Larger in height than the other letters throughout the text, these *v*'s are found in an evolved handwriting where the *d*'s are clear and in the form of musical notes. They express the strong receptive power of the antenna of cosmic energy which the triple heater of this writer possesses.

The other letters are round and gentle: only the *v*'s are sharp and drawn out, hence there is great acuity of hearing and clear, pure and precise reception.

This strange *v* displays the usual *v* *above* the base line and a loop twice as long below the line. The handwriting is very small, there is a distinct inferiority complex, but also the presence of great intuition. This writer, encouraged by this intuition, subconsciously would like to penetrate the invisible, but he is fearful (the *v* on the macrocosmic level corresponds to the kidneys and to fear). Instead of escaping from it, he entrenches himself further into the yin.

There is not one right angle in the form of this *v*. It begins with an inverted *s*, then descends into a garland that rises to form an *e* that is inclined to the left; it then reaches for the following letter. This triple heater is lacking in initiative and vivacity; it is also subject to states of depression. It is sluggish and gives the impression of being tired of living and reluctant to extend warmth to others.

This sample is from a 10 year old girl nicknamed "the Grapevine" by her classmates. She has this *v* all tangled up like a piece of yarn. Already at this age, her channels of irrigation and her nerves are in an unhealthy condition.

The *v* in this sample is dry, clearly formed, but it is the rising stroke that is thick and the descending one that is light. The sequence of pressure is thus reversed. This person seems gentle and distant (light descending stroke) but could become violent when interfered with (thick ascending stroke). The triple heater in this case is prone to conducting excesses of nervous tension.

Reaching far back, this *v* draws from the past to build up its momentum, it then descends with a heavy stroke and rises with a much shorter and lighter one. This triple heater is well aware of its own strength. It gears up, proceeds forcefully and then stops short. Where did the energy go? The clue is in the final stroke that forms the letter *e*. This indicates someone susceptible to impressions and likely to express themselves emotionally.

The Gall Bladder

Function: The gall bladder is a yang factory organ (its treasury is the liver). The gall bladder is husband (its wife is the stomach).

Latin
letter: *d*

Hebrew
letter: DALETH. The symbolic image is all abundant — nourishing things. It is a sign of divisible and divided nature, and expresses all ideas derived from the abundance born of division.

Egyptian
hieroglyph: The magnetic force of the human being — putting, placing, pushing, all manual labor.

Tarot: 4th major arcanum, the Emperor.

Role of the Gall Bladder

The gall bladder is a yang force. As a factory organ, it stimulates and struggles in opposition to its treasury organ (the liver), which accumulates. It fights to rid the organism of black bile, the enemy of the body. In accordance with this image, the Chinese call a great military leader Ta-Tann, which means Great Bladder.

Soulié de Morant tells us that the gall bladder is the Minister of Inner Rectitude. Decisiveness and sharpness result, for it is the sword of justice. And Ch'I-Po told the Yellow Emperor that, "the gall bladder occupies the position of an important and upright official who excels through his decisions and judgment."[32]

Psychology

The gall bladder is the sword of justice that cuts through and separates. Those who command too imperiously or abusively, and those who, on the contrary, do not use their swords through lack of authority both have defective gall bladders. It is as unhealthy to overstimulate an organ of combativity as it is to let it get rusty.

This organ-function is the Minister of Inner Rectitude; its healthy functioning is dependent on the energy used for the exercise of the will and the formation of judgement.

If its dominion is of a mental order, in the sense of authority and discrimination, it is also of a spiritual order: the gall bladder is similar to a mirror which both receives and reflects the rays of the sun. This organ-function takes in the cosmic energy that the triple heater receives from the cosmos. Its degree of clarity is of great importance in the realm of knowledge, and is on a plane clearly above that of the astral (ruled by the liver).

On the spiritual level, we may suppose that illness of the gall bladder results from the refusal, often subconscious, of the individual to come into contact with the unknown forces of the cosmos and of knowledge. It is a defense of the material body against spirit, which, through the cosmic vibrations, could liberate itself from material servitude via enlightenment.

Modern Western surgery does not acknowledge this spiritual role and is content to deal with the gall bladder according to its apparent physical condition. Should an illness occur, the gall bladder is often removed, since the organism is able to survive physically without it.

---

[32]See the *Yellow Emperor*, p. 133.

It is true that on the physical level the body can live without the gall bladder, however, on the level which presently concerns us, the triple heater is deprived of its organ of reception and can no longer function. Higher knowledge cannot be attained, for the current of enlightenment no longer has a channel for its vibrations.

Tarot: 4th major arcanum, the Emperor

 The Emperor wills, orders, and settles disputes with goodness and intelligence. He is the prince of a realm that rules over the concrete, he animates and governs the bodies. Seated on a golden cube, he is the symbol of the one who can possess the philosopher's stone. He corresponds to the grand architect of the masons. The tulip, the initiatory flower that corresponds to the lotus of the East, blooms at the Emperor's feet. It symbolizes the potential inherent in this arcanum.

Form of the *d*

This letter is probably the one that undergoes the most changes of form in handwriting. It represents at the same time: judgment, stability, and clarity of inner vision. Its meaning is difficult to perceive and calls for detailed study.

When the ascendent of the *d* forms an *l*, it indicates accumulation in order to give (LAMED = expansion); however, the gall bladder is yang not yin, it ought not to carry out the work of the liver, its treasury organ. Psychologically, this is a sign of deficient judgment.

This *d* with a small initial stroke reveals the flaccidity of the writer (the gall bladder governs energy); those who have energy and a firm footing are in need of no support. The letter opens toward the left and not at the top: the yang energy must make a detour before entering. The writer engages in self-contemplation before taking action (opening to the left), instead of receiving and listening (opening at the top). Medically speaking, this gall bladder is weak and in need of stimulation.

When *d* is in the form of a musical note, this gall bladder functions harmoniously and in a state of euphoria, from a medical viewpoint. Psychologically, this factory organ creates joy, discernment, clarity of vision. It is as clear as a mirror, receiving and reflecting vibrations harmoniously. The writer (a woman) attributes neither much importance nor any material value (absence of a return stroke to the base line) to the fruit of her efforts, she sees in them only music and poetry.

From the psychic viewpoint, when we observe all the letters relating to evolution, we could conclude that this writer has vision resulting from knowledge. Indeed, the liver[33] (*s, o, l*) functions well; the strokes of the handwriting denote sensitivity, the triple heater *v* is strong. As for the *d*'s, their vertical stroke indicates reaching toward the heights for cosmic vibrations. These well-apprehended yang currents descend and fall upon the oval of a cosmic egg, which is

---

[33]The liver is the Temple of Forces of seership.

analogous to the macrocosm; this oval is clear (loop of the *d*); therefore, it clearly transmits the signals received.

DALETH is the Emperor who settles things with firmness, but also with goodness and intelligence. The intelligence of DALETH is brought by the force of yang: but here the writer opposes it by a horizontal stroke that creates a ceiling. The will is weak and lacks elevation of intelligence, the "ceiling" on the *d* blocks or limits it. Symbolically this Emperor has a sword of justice whose blade is strangely bent out of shape.

DALETH corresponds to the number 4, and here we have a Daleth with two bars, or a *d* with two legs spread out. This corresponds to the Priestess of the tarot. This letter stands out among a lilliputian script stacked in the middle of the page with large blank spaces at the top, left side, and bottom of the page. The writer has a marked inferiority complex. His will is reduced by half in relation to the norm and expresses itself in the symbol of the veil of the Priestess, that is, "he prefers to withdraw rather than to lead."

This *d* reproduces the form of the Moon: it indicates that judgment is greatly influenced by an overactive imagination.

Here we can read *e* + *l* in the *d*. It is the great military leader who, far from being Emperor, is above all women (*e* = HE = cup) and, who sacrifices himself (LAMED). It is a gall bladder that has given up the fight out of fatigue and discouragement. The doctors have just eliminated it, as this person had surgery shortly after writing this.

Throughout this text there are alternatively large clear and majestic *d*'s and small blocked *d*'s with a vertical stroke in the form of an *l*. This writer is subject to serious gall bladder attacks with an excess of bile. Psychologically, he goes through phases of "Good Emperor" and "Bad Emperor." He loves money, has some, but overwhelmed by fear of want, soon blocks himself and loses his good judgment. So the medical practitioners "empty" the gall bladder, he sees clearly, and starts all over again!

The Liver

Function:	The liver is a yin treasury organ (its yang factory is the gall bladder.) The liver is husband (its wife is the spleen-pancreas).
Latin letter:	*s*
Hebrew letter: ס	SAMEKH. The image of the bow whose cord sings in the hand.
Egyptian hieroglyph: ſ	The tie between the material and the astral plane, this is the tie that joins the two panels of

a closed door and prevents them from being opened. Those who have drawn the bolt have manifested the will and fixed a state of affairs according to their desire and power.

Tarot: *s* = 15th major arcanum, the Devil.

Latin
letter: *o*

Hebrew
letter: AYIN. It is the VAU[34] in its purely physical relationship. It is a sign of all that is false, twisted, perverse, and evil.

Egyptian
hieroglyph: Action originating in human beings or exterior forces originating in them.

Tarot: *o* = 16th major arcanum, the Tower.

Latin
letter: *l*

Hebrew
letter: LAMED. The symbolic image of an arm, the wing of a bird, all that that extends and unfolds itself. It is a sign of an expansive movement that applies to all ideas of extension, elevation, and possession.

Tarot: *l* = 12th major arcanum, the Hanged Man.

---

[34]VAU = triple heater, direct contact with the vibrations of the cosmos.

Role of the Liver

The kidney-bladder couple concentrates liquids, while the liver-pancreas concentrates matter.

The role of the liver is that of a treasury organ. It is passive and static in its integration of energy (the dynamic aspect being reserved for the factory organ). By its function of concentrating matter, it gives the organism its tone.

Soulié de Morant defines the liver as the Minister of the Chiefs of Staff, elaborating plans and strategies. And in Ch'I-Po's answer to the Yellow Emperor, "the liver has the functions of a military leader who excels in his strategic planning."[35] The external analyzer of the liver is sight.

Psychology

A liver in perfect condition brings lucidity and possibilities of clairvoyance, and so, of discernment. When it is blocked with bile one can no longer see clearly. A defective state or the congestion of this organ can bring about aggressivity or a great moral fatigue that corresponds to physical fatigue (the liver gives the organism its tone and the spleen-pancreas, its spouse, forms its structure).

A malfunctioning liver can be compared symbolically to an arm that cannot extend itself fully, a wing that cannot unfold itself. Egotism is what paralyzes it, concentration is turned toward the ego.

Psyche

The ancients designated the liver as the seat of "seeing." We use this word in the sense of the possibility of contact between the astral and intermediary zones. We are not here on the planes of the cosmos and knowledge—these modes of perception remain the privilege of those who know how to

---

[35]See the *Yellow Emperor*, p. 133.

enter into contact with the invisible by way of the triple heater.

In support of the claim of a correspondence between the liver and the astral planes, I will ask the reader to consider the Nei-Ching, which states that the liver opens into the eyes.[36] The eyes see the darkness and the mystery of the sky and discover the Tao, the Straight Path, amongst the human race. Also consider the Egyptian hieroglyph which means— in its initiatory sense—SAMEKH is the link between the material and the astral planes. It would be difficult to find a more exact definition of the role of the liver in relation to vision. In Africa, to this day, the shamans fast for the three days preceding magical ceremonies to empty the liver to protect themselves from any "backfire." They call the liver the "Temple of the Forces."

• • •

The three Arcana of the Tarot that correspond to the three letters pertaining to the liver constitute a lesson in caution and wisdom. They warn of the dangers of magic and of selfishness.

Tarot: 15th major arcanum, the Devil; *s*

This card represents the correspondence between the astral and the etheric bodies by way of the cosmic currents. It shows the limitless power of high magic, which comes to the one who knows and puts it to use wisely; otherwise, he will be forever chained to its pedestal. On the material plane, this card corresponds to the money which one earns and concentrates.

---

[36]The eyes, which in their capacity to see outwardly, also esoterically represent the inward seeing of seership. See Kaptchuk's, *The Web That Has No Weaver*, p. 61.

Tarot: 16th major arcanum, the Tower; *o*

This shows the lot that befalls those who enter life with impure motives and a lack of discernment. The ego of the egotist is similar to this crumbling tower. It is also the symbol of the traumatic backlash that awaits the black magician and to which the Catholics gave the name of punishment.

Tarot: 12th major arcanum, the Hanged Man; *l*

The card of sacrifice and of renunciation. It is the trump that teaches the secret of the path.

> The Hanged Man is bound, not as an instinctive or blind believer, but as a wise who has discerned the vanity of individual ambitions and has understood the wealth of the heroic sacrifices which aspires towards total oblivion of self.[37]

Apparently inactive, the Hanged Man acquires in fact a wealth of unlimited energy. On his clothing there are two moons. The one on the left is waning and red; it reminds us of the humility which the seer must have. The moon on the right is white, to remind us that the interpretation of the impressions which we receive depends upon purity of being.

---

[37] *The Tarot of the Magicians*, p. 110.

The liver works in a yin fashion, the Hanged Man has an inward action.

Forms of the *s, o,* and *l*

These three letters must be studied together with flexibility. They confirm and complement each other, as the tarot explains. Clairvoyance is a delicate thing to understand, its reflection in the letters requires an intelligently guided examination.

The *s* corresponds to two letters in the Hebrew alphabet and in the Egyptian hieroglyphs: SHIN and SAMEKH. The interpretation in the sense of SHIN is quite rarely used — it will be described in chapter 7. Here, we will study SAMEKH in relation to the liver.

This *s*, which plunges below the base line, gives the image of one who stashes away his secret (SAMEKH = the staff) in the earth to make it invisible. The writer sinks more deeply into matter and this *s* is often the sign of a repressed aggressivity that retracts its claws. This view will be further confirmed if, in the same handwriting, the *l*'s are blocked or in the form of a simple stroke. On the other hand, if the *l* is clearly formed, it indicates a writer who loves secrets (without necessarily being able to keep one!).

This *s*, written higher than the other letters, raises its head high transforming itself into an antenna for clairvoyance and telepathy. It indicates a treasury liver that brings full satisfaction and denotes a clear and healthy discernment that is above taking sides.

Loose and open at the bottom, these *s*'s are very susceptible to the influence of yin and therefore to the lunar. Whatever is exaggeratedly open becomes prey to illusions and, on
the astral plane, there is great danger.

If, at the same time, the *o*'s are filled in or malformed,
as well as the *l*'s, the writer should be warned against all
spiritualistic or psychic experiences, and even anything pertaining to an unwholesome imagination. According to its
Hebraic meaning, the *s* is a bow whose string hums. In this
particular *s*, not only is the string missing, but the form also
evokes a bolt that is wide open: there would seem to be little
disposition for keeping secrets.

This *s* is on the base line, well sealed on three sides, but
very open to the left: it directs its energy toward the ego and
toward selfishness. It indicates a treasury organ that provides
its factory with nothing because it keeps the treasure for
itself.

In the same sample, the *o*'s were very open also, but at
the top. We may conclude from this that laziness and selfishness are strong, but neither is due to meanness because the
looseness of the letters excludes aggressivity; the preference is
toward letting go rather than fighting. Yet, the tone of the
organism feels the effects of this poor concentration, which is
partially responsible for great physical fatigue and lazy
character.

This *l* with a filled-in loop is symbolic of a congested
liver. If, in the same text, there are *l*'s with clear loops, this
congestion is only temporary or accidental.

ℓℓ

This *o*, with two upper knots, is often found in the handwriting of nuns or of people whose mysticism is great but lacking in scope or real elevation. Knots are an obstacle to development. It is the manifestation, physically, of a liver that concentrates badly.

Psychologically, it indicates two tendencies which can be determined according to the form of the *l*'s. For example, if the *l*'s are filled in or very small, it indicates that through misguided asceticism, voluntary privations, or sacrifices (LAMED), the writer has made of her life an Ivory Tower (*o* = Tower of the tarot). Sacrificing everything to her ideal, she thinks she has reached a summit, but it is all for naught since she cannot, spiritually speaking, even raise her arm (*l* underdeveloped). However, it does indicate a strong sense of discipline and great self-mastery because the *o* is tied to the preceding and following letters by knots. However, if the *l*'s are open and large, there is self-sacrifice and giving of the self (LAMED = expansion) but the *o*, being the Tower and therefore death, indicates fear, consciously or unconsciously, of the hereafter. Knots are always indicative of a problem.

△

This triangular *o* takes the form of the symbol for Fire in alchemy. This letter form takes on a different meaning according to the handwriting in which it is found; that is in the handwriting of evolved people, those who seek to elevate themselves, it is a symbol of enthusiasm, of the sacred fire. It is the sign of vision which, in a certain sense, approaches knowledge. In a materialistic person, the *o* takes on the meaning of the Tower. A tower must have four sides and this one has but three: moreover, a pointed fire sign will inevitably attract lightning: it is a warning of possible backlash after visions and of the risk of madness.

In any case, if the *o* is larger than the other letters in the text, it loses the meaning of fire and takes on that of vanity: those who make of ego a unique tower that others cannot help but notice. The symbolic meaning of the Hebraic AYIN is "all that is false, perverse."

The Lungs

Function: The lungs are a yin treasury (their yang factory is the large intestine). The lungs are wife (their husband is the heart).

Latin
letter: *h*

Hebrew
letter: HETH. This letter offers the image of a kind of equilibrium. It is the symbol of elementary existence, it represents the realm of the human being, of work, of that which demands effort, care, fatigue.

Egyptian
hieroglyph: The field where we must do our work. Human beings transform raw matter into organized matter.

Tarot: 11th major arcanum, Justice.

Role of the Lungs

The lungs are the energizing factors of nutrition. By means of the nose, which is the mouth of the lungs, energy/oxygen enters the organism and gives it vital movement and expansion.

Smell is the external analyzer for the lungs, it informs them of the quality of the outer environment/air, serving as antennae of sensitivity whose seat is the large intestine, the factory-organ.

The lungs are the entry system for air, and they also provide the exit: toxic air is expelled from the body by this passageway to the outside. This dual role of the lungs is highlighted in Soulié de Morant's definition for he said that the Minister of the Great Leader, the flowered cover of the five treasury organs, connects the interior and the exterior. Ch'I-Po replied to the Yellow Emperor that the lungs are the Ministers who supervise the conduct of the administrators of jurisdiction and regulations.[38]

Psychology

By drawing in air, the lungs swell. The saying, "an inflated ego," takes on its full meaning here, and is summed up in the word pride. On the other hand, a shy person "has a deflated ego and withdraws into his shell." The lungs promote vital and psychic energy. We can be bursting with good health or any lack of balanced energy can give us the feeling of being drained.

The sense of smell, an antenna of sensitivity, keeps us on the alert: it gives "flair" to those who know how to use it; it is know-how guided by flair.

The importance of breathing is well known in Yoga. It is an unlimited field of development, for we can expand it through effort and personal study.

Also note that the two lungs stress the idea of balance.

---

[38]See the *Yellow Emperor*, p. 133.

Tarot: 8th major arcanum, Justice

The woman on this tarot card is passive (she is seated), yet active (she is facing outward with open eyes), and she represents Justice. In one hand, she holds scales whose platforms are both at the same level, the symbol of balance, and with the other hand she holds a raised sword, the symbol of her active Authority. The action represented by this card is the movement generative of life, order, organization, energy. It is the image of the role of the lungs.

Form of the *h*

A large, strong, well-delineated *h* is expressive of someone who is broad-chested. If the form of this letter is exaggerated, it is because pride is involved: "He's full of himself," as they say.

An *h* with a filled-in loop and a lower portion with sharp angles indicates that the lungs are poorly oxygenated, as a result of which the blood is polluted and anemic; hence there is a tendency to worry and low self-esteem. Getting by is not the predominant quality of this writer.

When the *h* is clearly formed, but without an upper loop, the oxygenation of the lungs is restrained. Here there is no trace of pride, nor is there excessive humility; it is balance with a slight tendency toward self-depreciation.

An *h* with an extra upper loop not attached to the body of the letter itself is the sign of psychic respiration which, through need of an ideal, or through a desire to travel off the beaten path, seeks air in more elevated spheres. The emotivity and sensitivity of this writer is strong in all areas of the spirit. Her vital energy is excellent.

The form of this *h* is the sign of someone who, through self-depreciation, is fearful of life.

This *h* denotes great self-esteem (the loop is prominent), but also a certain aggressivity because the lower portion is angular, emerging from the base line and not from the crossing of the upper loop.

The Stomach

Function: The stomach is a yang factory organ (its yin treasury is the spleen-pancreas). The stomach is wife (its husband is the gall bladder).

Latin
letter: *b*

Hebrew
letter: BETH. The symbolic image is the dwelling, the
               interior. It is a sign of an active and inner
ב   action.

Egyptian
hieroglyph: It is the organ of direct contact with matter, and,
               as such, is subject to its laws; it takes upon itself
⌐   all the material weight of the body by allowing
               the upper parts, and the head in particular, to
               raise themselves freely toward the heavens.

Tarot: 2nd major arcanum, the High Priestess.

Role of the Stomach

The stomach is the factory-organ which analyzes that which
comes from the exterior, ruminating and digesting it. In its
healthy state this factory causes hunger, for it is in constant
need of rumination. Work here is proof of physical balance:
"it's running smoothly," as they say, and if one has an "empty
stomach," it must quickly be filled. It is the sign of an inward
and active movement which calls for and accepts matter coming from the outside. But when it malfunctions, it causes
revulsion and ulceration.

A well-known Arab proverb says: "It is the stomach that
carries the feet." The feet are the pedestal for the bone structure, they support the body's weight; the stomach is the factory of the digestive system[39] which creates the physical condition and the structure of the bones. Its healthy functioning
has a direct relationship to the physical condition of the
Being.

---

[39]See the digestive system, chapter 5.

Soulié de Morant wrote that the stomach is the Minister of the Granaries, the sea of the five treasury organs and six factories, the source of all energies. And Ch'I-Po replied to the Yellow Emperor that the stomach acts like the administrator of the public granaries and satisfies the five tastes (the Economic Resources).[40]

Psychology

What does the stomach correspond to mentally? The Egyptian BETH indicates a leg which should permit us to lift ourselves toward the heavens through *intelligence*. And what is intelligence if not mental rumination?

Stomach and intelligence are synonymous. This key of Chinese medicine leads us to consider two different aspects of intelligence, or rather two ways of looking at it. First, the intelligence that is turned toward the spirit and that tends towards Wisdom; second, the intelligence that is turned toward matter and that, evolutionarily speaking, amounts to stupidity—there is some mistaken orientation.

In any case, BETH is the intelligence which forms the elements for the edification of the soul. And here we would point out that according to Chinese thought:

♦ the stomach forms the intelligence of the soul;

♦ the spleen-pancreas forms the intelligence of ideas;

♦ the liver forms the intelligence of the organs;

♦ the lungs form the intelligence of the cells.

Intelligence is such a relative matter that before you form a judgment about it, it is recommended that you meditate upon the ideas briefly noted above.

---

[40]See the *Yellow Emperor*, p. 133.

Psyche

When it is in good health, the stomach accepts matter from the exterior, and we experience calm and fulfillment: our ideas are clear, the intelligence has a "good appetite."

It is quite another matter when this organ refuses what comes from the exterior. Nothing works, we become irritable, aggressive, we take it out on others, who will conclude that we are "revolted" (*ulcéré* in French). Psychic anguish overwhelms everything, causing trouble and disorder: intelligence no longer forms the soul; the feet no longer carry the being toward wisdom.

Tarot: 2nd major arcanum, the High Priestess

Outwardly passive, the High Priestess ruminates on her thoughts. Her eyes are veiled, the book that she holds is closed. All her work is an inner and profound rumination. Her intelligence is great; she is among those who act silently and powerfully. The keys she holds are made of gold and silver: one is solar (Sun = spleen-pancreas, the treasury organ of the stomach); the other is lunar (Moon = stomach, factory organ of the spleen-pancreas).[41] They symbolize the balanced inner and mental work which leads to intelligence of the soul and to knowledge

Form of the *b*

The *b* is made of a loop followed by an opening directed upward, and so toward the yang. It feeds upon light,

---

[41]BETH (and the stomach, which corresponds to it) is yang. Here it is not a matter of current, but of astrological influence. Indeed, one must distinguish on the one hand the chinese currents—yang, solar; yin lunar—and on the other, the planetary and zodiacal influences that place the stomach under the dominion of the sign of Cancer and of the Moon, which rules this sign.

warmth, and beauty. It is a letter of spirituality. Physically, the stomach receives its nourishment from the outside, where there is light — the stomach itself being in the dark — ruminates on it and sends to the spleen-pancreas, its treasury, the elements needed by the digestive system. These two letters (*b* and *q*) will therefore often be in correspondence.

A harmonious *b* brings about equilibrium, joy, peace, and elevation of feeling, intelligence of the soul. A pain-free stomach functions without worry.

h

This *b*, which is closed to the yang influence yet not to the yin, turns away from the Sun and toward the mirages of the Moon. When the form of a letter changes in direction in this way, its sense of dynamism degenerates: it exposes the organism to all that is evil and unhealthy in the lunar psyche. Here the stomach is subject to cramps, which over the years can provoke an ulcer. The individual becomes cranky and inordinately anxious, which is why we say that this person is revolted ("ulcéré" in French). At the same time, this form of *b* is often a sign of intuition.

The curve of this stroke does not turn back on itself; it is connected to the letters that follow and represents great mental and psychic sensitivity (yin influence) without connoting any physical anguish (the letter is not isolated). The stomach functions no matter what.

The horizontal figure-eight is the symbol for a continuous electrical current. This symbol is found on the hats of the Magician and of the figure of Strength (8th major arcanum) in the tarot—a reminder that these currents come from the mind.

We know that *b* is the stomach. Given this, we would conclude that a *b* in the form of an 8 indicates a stomach burn created by the individual's mind. The mind (cerebral system) is the master of the nerves in Chinese medicine: this is therefore a clear case of stomach burn (acidic condition, ulcer, etc.) caused by a nervous condition. Digestion is impaired, and the subject is prone to nervous aggressivity.

This *b* in the form of an *l* indicates that the person is aspiring to evolution (the loop is present and is clear), but has trouble ruminating, and therefore meditating (the stroke does not continue upward). Physically, food has a tendency to pass through the stomach too quickly and so cannot sufficiently be assimilated.

This *b*, simplified to the extreme without losing any of its essential characteristics, is shaped like a musical note and is symbolic of song, of spiritual and digestive harmony. The rest of the handwriting confirms this impression. It is a rather rare form, for the general tendency is to modify the form of a letter in the direction of materialism rather than of spirituality.

The *b* is the letter of spiritual evolution, our reaching toward the ideal. Here the impulse, being interrupted by a horizontal bar, comes to an abrupt stop. The BETH is yang, but this one, being open to the yin, is prey to psychic anguish and despair. A person who writes in this manner, often will be prone to suicidal thoughts.[42]

The Spleen-Pancreas

Function: The spleen-pancreas is a yin treasury organ (its factory organ is the stomach).
The spleen-pancreas is wife (its husband is the liver).

Latin
letter: *q*

Hebrew
letter: QOPH. The symbolic image represents a cutting weapon, everything that serves as an instrument, which defends us, or facilitates effort. It designates force and constraint.

Egyptian
hieroglyph: Matter without form which must be worked.

Tarot: 19th major arcanum, the Sun.

---

[42]Handwriting of Brigitte Bardot, in "Astres," Paris, October, 1961, #162.

Role of the Spleen-Pancreas:

The spleen-pancreas is the organ-function that forms the structure of the being. The stomach absorbs nutrients coming from the exterior, but it is its treasury, the spleen-pancreas, that accumulates them, like the stockroom of a store that must meet the needs of its clientele.

The Chinese say: "The five viscera all obtain their stamina from the spleen; the spleen is the foundation of the existence of the five viscera." The spleen corresponds to Saturn; in Chinese medicine this is called the Great Director.

Soulié de Morant said that the spleen-pancreas is the Minister who points out errors and speaks of equity, or, as medical students in China are taught today, "the spleen rules the raising of the pure". It is also commonly known that "the spleen rules transformation and transportation. The spleen is the crucial link by which food is transformed into Qui and Blood."[43]

Psychology

The spleen-pancreas is the organ-function that forms ideas and the intelligence of ideas. It is ideas that form the personality and we all use this treasure in our own way.

There is a popular French expression, "se dilater la rate" (literally, to dilate one's spleen, i.e., to split one's sides with laughter), which designates a state of joy, laughter, and plenitude. It is a minister without worries, his "granaries" are full, his ideas sound, his intelligence brings him serenity: the sun shines in. The opposite expression: "se faire du mauvais sang," means literally to make bad blood for oneself, that is, to worry. We also say, "to vent one's spleen," meaning to fully express temper. To have spleen in English means a black mood, as well as referring to the organ itself. The ideas are disturbed, something is missing, anguish has set in.

---

[43] *The Web That Has No Weaver*, pp. 57–58.

Psychologically we can identify two forms of despair provoked by a deficient spleen-pancreas. One is caused by the polluted condition of the blood which stimulates and overloads the liver and gall bladder, obstructing spiritual faculties that correspond to these two organ functions, thus giving rise to animosity and aggressivity. Another happens when the anemic blood no longer provides its factory, the stomach, with the necessary activity; the organs are numbed and the subject is filled with spleen from which his deficient physical state cannot help to extract him. There is languor or neurasthenia.

Tarot: 19th major arcanum, the Sun

As the Sun is the center of our planetary system, the spleen-pancreas is the foundation for the existence of our viscera and for the structure of the organism. It is the card of agreement, of harmony, which, like the spleen-pancreas when it is healthy, brings serenity and fulfillment. The solar spirit is made of intelligence and wisdom.

Form of the *q*

This letter consists of a circle which can have an opening, and of a descending vertical bar. I say bar because a loop is exceptional.

Abnormally large in the text, this *q* is braced on the left by an initial stroke (an unnecessary one, for the letter would stand without it). It is also open to the left. Because of its disproportionately large size, the round part tends to give an impression of fullness, but the leftward opening revises this idea of serenity, since a fulfilled being has no need to "open" a window onto himself, being free of problems. It would be toward the right, toward others and the future that he would open himself if he were really at peace.

This form reveals anxiety of an intimate and emotional kind (the roundness relates to it to the letter *a*, the emotional center). This writer is afraid of not being able to "stand it." He seeks a support to shore up his spleen. His ideas are nostalgic and not very consistent during periods of depression.

The form of this *q* indicates a spleen-pancreas that is making an effort (heavy vertical stroke) in order to function well, but unable to do so, it seeks help by reaching up toward the following letter. This person has good ideas, but has difficulty materializing, and effort is required to bring them to completion.

This vertical bar is completely deformed: the spleen-pancreas, far from expanding with joy within, twists like a worm. The functioning of this organ is deficient. However, the mind is quick, original, and has strong intuition (yin opening). The psyche is in a state of torment. This person dwells continuously on family problems. It is a Great Director with a worried brow, not an Olympian calm.

9

Throughout the text, the *q*'s adopt an interlaced design with fantastic arabesques. If we consider that the spleen-pancreas is a treasury-organ that structures ideas, we can say that in this case there is no lack of ideas, but, because of their complexity, they require long hours of explanation. In any case, the "inventory" is abundant (the spleen is the administrator of the public granaries). And as Ch'I-Po told the Yellow Emperor,

> These twelve officials should not fail to assist one another. When the Monarch is intelligent and enlightened, there is peace and contentment among his subjects; they can thus beget offspring, bring up their children, earn a living and lead a long and happy life. And because there are no more dangers and perils, the earth is considered glorious and prosperous.

> But when the Monarch is not intelligent and enlightened, the twelve officials become dangerous and perilous; the use of Tao (the Right Way) is obstructed and blocked, and Tao no longer circulates the warnings against physical excesses.[44]

---

[44]See the *Yellow Emperor*, p. 133–134.

4

The Three Principles

The three Chinese principles that we consider to be the most remarkable and interesting for their symbolism in graphology and their psychological correspondences are:

1) the husband-wife principle;

2) the factory-treasury principle;

3) the mother-son principle.

According to the Chinese way, the husband-wife principle works in this manner—the wife organs are governed, while the husband organs are the governors. Here is how, two by two, the twelve organ-functions harmonize[1] according to the Chinese pulse[2] and independently of any of the systems.[3]

Husband	*Wife*
Kidney	Circulation-Sexuality
Bladder	Triple Heater

---

[1]Harmony on the basis of a 120 degree angle on the circle of energy comparable to the trine between planets in astrology.

[2]Left wrist = the husbands; right wrist = the wives.

[3]We stress the fact that the husband-wife principle harmonizes the organ functions by pairs and that the process is not the same within the four systems (chapter 5).

Liver	Spleen-Pancreas
Gall Bladder	Stomach
Heart	Lungs
Small Intestine	Large Intestine

Soulié de Morant explains that each of the organs relating to the left wrist—the husband—dominates the corresponding organ reflected in the right wrist—the Wife. Dominates—that is to say—gives it life, or more specifically, is essential to its operation. Conversely, each organ reflected in the right wrist (the wife) endangers its corresponding left wrist organ (the husband) to endanger means to force it to make extraordinary efforts, beyond the limits of its power, and thus there is the risk of lesions.[4]

As applied to graphology we have observed and verified the following cases:

Liver/spleen-pancreas (husband-wife)
In a woman's handwriting:

the husband organ (liver o) is wide open and takes the form of an a;

the wife organ (pancreas q) is strongly drawn, very variable in its form, and, throughout the text, it seeks the support of the following letter.

What we have here is a wife whose moods are as variable as her ideas, (different forms of the q) filled with spleen (the

---

[4]George Soulié de Morant, *Chinese Acupuncture* (2 vols.), Paul Zmiewski, ed. (Brookline, MA: Paradigm Publishers, 1990).

marked opening of the letter) and who languishes (or seeks support from the following letter). Because of her spleen, this wife urges her husband to extraordinary efforts in his work, until, weary of carrying the load for two, he cries out for mercy: the *o* transforms itself into an *a*, the letter of love and of life. The liver is the Minister of the Armies; he elaborates strategies. Here, the Minister of the Armies is under-assisted and has only one strategy—to long for peace (*o* into *a*).

The writer in question is characterized by a taciturn spleen and listlessness that take precedence over the desire for action. The disorganization of this spleen-pancreas function can take the form of cancer.

The teachings of medical astrology tell us that a proliferation of cells due to the influence of Jupiter (the planet of expansion which rules the liver) prevents the rational structuring of forms by Saturn (which rules the pancreas) and thereby brings about a cancer.

Kidney/circulation-sexuality (husband-wife)

In a woman's handwriting the kidney husband organ *t* had a vertical bar that plunged below the base line of the other letters, and the *v*'s took on the closed shape of the *o*'s.

The circulation-sexuality wife organ *j*, by its size and prominent form leaves no room for anyone but herself (she considers herself as two: *j* + *e*—*Je* in French means "I"). To resist the invader, the husband burrows into the ground or withdraws into himself, renouncing all decisions, for his wife sees only herself and is "too full of herself".

The sexual mentality of the writer is misguided. She is the sort of wife who squelches her husband, all the while thinking herself to be victim of her spouse's viciousness. Physically, she suffers from kidney trouble and heavy menstrual flow; there is pronounced ovarian malfunction.

In another handwriting sample, note that the vertical bars of this *t*, in a man's handwriting, are small, thin, without sharp angles and they float above the baseline.

The *v*'s extend initially toward the preceding letters with a light stroke then descend at an angle with a thick stroke that touches the baseline and lightly ascends to extend itself to the following letter. At the onset of action, the decisive will is strong and authoritarian, but when reality sets in (the baseline) it loses its vigor and weakens. The kidney meridian suffers from this swing between ardor and shyness. It causes it pain and leads to kidney stones. The husband, the kidneys, puts on a powerful front, but it is in fact weak and in pain.

The *j*'s are written according to the school model; they are a bit small but well formed and very consistent.

$\boldsymbol{\ell}$

The *e*'s are filled in with ink. This organ wife's reasoning is a result of the husband's attitude: a well-written *t*, although frail, indicates good reasoning full of common sense (well-formed *j*'s) but a nervous outburst (*v*) from the kidneys creates a state of anxiety (*e*'s filled in) and disturbs the psychological balance by bringing on a state of depression.

In another sample from a young woman in her thirties, the handwriting is large and prominent—it lets itself be noticed. The vertical *t* stem nearly touches the line above and goes also below the baseline. The will is here well established and affirms itself come hell or high water. This causes the kidneys to contract and be in pain. This woman is often seen placing her hands over her kidneys and bemoaning the pain that she undergoes—yet, no sooner said than she's off again.

Her *j*'s are irregular but they are all very strong. Reasoning is decisive, forceful, and soundly made known.

In conclusion then: the husband (kidneys) is strong, imposing and willful; this leads it to contract and causes lower back pain. Her reasoning is decisive (*j*'s very large) and not subject to anyone's influence. This organ wife is basically masculine. This is a couple that proceeds like a bulldozer, going forward no matter what and crushing everything in its path. The sexuality of this woman is male and aggressive, but at the same time feminine—for the ovaries function well (clear *e*'s); this woman was in fact pregnant at the time this handwriting sample was analyzed.

Liver/spleen-pancreas (husband-wife)

8

In this sample of a woman's handwriting the *s*'s have a strange look about them: this one takes on the form of an 8; it begins and encloses toward the left. The contents of this *s* lend importance to the past and to matter. The liver thus lacks in discernment and is preoccupied with its own problems. This can cause it to be hardened through congestion.

σ

The *o*'s are like a swollen sac that is well tied; there is no way to look into it. The liver is secretive and does not extend itself.

l l

The *l*'s are inconsistently made and half the time are filled with bile. The husband liver is not easy to deal with!

q q

Poor Qoph and poor wife. She does not understand her husband, and her own weakness prevents her from effectively intervening — made all the more difficult when the husband is ill, secretive, and hard to deal with. Morality and consciousness have trouble expressing themselves. Within this couple it is the husband (liver) that dominates, but he does so badly for he acts on his own as an individual and not as a couple; the blood (liver and pancreas) is impure and the red blood cells are weak.

In another example of a liver/spleen-pancreas couple we find these three *s*'s within the text! The irregularities in the letter, both in form and size, indicate the liver's inconsistencies.

The *o*'s are as irregular as the *s*'s.

The *l*'s float above the baseline and do not maintain a consistent shape throughout. Nonetheless, none of them are filled in with ink, which means that the problem is not a question of the bile being on fire.

The *q*'s however, are neat and simply formed. The ideas are clear and so is consciousness and morality. The husband is a weakling, indecisive and unstable. The liver lets itself be guided by shrewdness when it comes to action. It is also very prone to jealousy with all of the emotion and hostility that this entails. The wife, on the other hand, is decisive, perceives the faults, points them out and does not want to hear that the system is fatigued. She also manufactures strong red and white blood cells. A weak husband and a strong wife; in Chinese medicine this indicates an obstructed condition and is considered to be an unfortunate state of affairs.

Heart/lungs (husband-wife)

In a male writing sample: t

the heart husband organ *t* has very irregular horizontal bars, but they are always neat and small;

h

the lung wife organ *h* always has blacked-in upper loops or none at all, that is, made of a single stroke.

This cardio-respiratory system is defective. Oxygenation of the lungs is weak and the heart suffers from the poor functioning of its assistant. The regularity of the *t* bars, which are never missing, shows that the heart suffers but it is not to blame. In the mind of this writer, his wife is at fault and keeps him from "breathing."

The Factory-Treasury Principle

Here is how the factory-treasury[5] principle is set up according to the Chinese[6] left-right pulse opposition:

Yin Treasury	*Yang Factory*
Lungs	Large Intestine
Heart	Small Intestine
Spleen-Pancreas	Stomach
Liver	Gall Bladder
Circulation-Sexuality	Triple Heater
Kidneys	Bladder

Soulié de Morant defines them as: Factory-Organs — yang (Fu). The Chinese character *Fu* is composed of the

---

[5]Deep pulse = treasury organ; superficial pulse = factory organ.
[6]Dr. Choain, *Voie Rationelle de la Medecine Chinoise*, p. 277.

elements "flesh — man working — beneath a roof," hence the factory-organs. They are so named because they transform into energy and blood the material they receive from the exterior.

Treasury-Organs — yin (Tsang): The Chinese character *Tsang* is composed of the elements "flesh — treasure." They preside over the purification and circulation of the blood.

Treasury and factory complement each other and have clearly defined roles. A change in rhythm can upset the physical and psychic states. Here are some graphological examples:

Kidney/bladder (treasury-factory)

When you see handwriting with absolutely identical forms for the *n*'s and the *v*'s, consider the following indications:

v = VAU = kidneys = treasury: concentrates and establishes barriers;

n = NUN = bladder = factory: eliminatory energy, conditions the spiritual balance.

Here it is the *n* that has taken on the form of the *v*: the bladder, therefore, takes on the role of a treasury and not that of a factory, since it models itself on the kidneys in trying to concentrate instead of eliminate. The organism is thus faced with two organ-functions that are static and that harm rather than complement each other.

Physically, this will eventually cause bladder trouble with pain and difficulty in elimination. Psychically, the sexual mentality (a psychic reflection of the kidney-bladder) is not free. There are blockages, pressures, inhibitions — a fact largely confirmed by the form of the letters of the circulation-sexuality — the third organ function of the cerebral system[7] (which is there to control the precision of the factory-treasury principle).

---

[7]See chapter 5.

Liver/gall bladder (treasury-factory)

In one woman's handwriting, the letters corresponding to the liver and gall bladder organ-functions showed the *l*'s and *o*'s malformed, with often irregular shapes and sometimes with the loop of the *l* filled in.

The *d*'s, on the other hand, have a breadth and form that shows them to be "at full steam" with an excess of power (hook-like curve).

By working too intensely, the gall bladder is a factory organ which exhausts its liver treasury organ. The latter no longer presides over the blood's circulation and purification, as should be the case with a treasury organ, for it is exhausted. It is a poor Minister of the Armies and the gall bladder reacts with bitterness.

Even if in other parts the handwriting gives an indication of intuition and a desire for evolution, we may say, a priori, that the liver, the seat of vision, "sees nothing" and that the gall bladder, the mirror of the triple heater, takes its own work as something "sent" from above.

Lungs/large intestine (treasury-factory)

In a man's handwriting:

We find *h*'s that are very small relative to the surrounding letters. The ascender is looped and the hook at the bottom is square-shaped.

$\int$

The *p*'s form a closed pocket.
h = lung = treasury organ.
p = intestines = factory organ.

In this form of shrunken *h*, the lungs receive a minimum of material from the outside, that is to say, little oxygen: their role as treasury is badly carried out.

Consequently, the intestines, operating like a prudent factory, want to keep the little that they receive and so are constipated. If we take this exit system further, we necessarily observe that if the lungs receive little, they also expell little; if both of these organ-functions hold back, there is asphyxiation.

Medically, the blood is impoverished and the vital energy is mediocre. Psychologically, the Minister of Finances and Transmissions has a guilty conscience, he underestimates (or over-estimates) himself by creating cause for worry and sorrow through bad management. As a result the sensitivity suffers.

Mother-Son Principle

This principle follows the sequence of the organ-functions in the flow of energy through the day/night cycle. An organ function has for a mother the organ which precedes it and for a son the one which follows it. In keeping with Chinese medicine, we can say that the energy of a meridian comes from the one which precedes it and flows into the one which follows it. In the interest of clarity, I provide Table 1:

Table 1. Mother-Son Energy.

Mother	Observed Organ	Son
Stomach	Spleen-Pancreas	Heart
Spleen-Pancreas	Heart	Small Intestine
Heart	Small Intestine	Bladder
Small Intestine	Bladder	Kidney
Bladder	Kidney	Circulation-Sexuality
Kidney	Circulation-Sexuality	Triple Heater
Circulation-Sexuality	Triple Heater	Gall Bladder
Triple Heater	Gall Bladder	Liver
Gall Bladder	Liver	Lungs
Liver	Lungs	Large Intestine
Lungs	Large Intestine	Stomach
Large Intestine	Stomach	Spleen-Pancreas

In graphology we will use the Mother-Son principle when seeking out the reason for the weakness of an organ-function whose cause we have not been able to locate. If a mother organ-function is overloaded, it is quite rare for the one that follows to be in good shape; similarly, a weakened son organ-function will need to nourish itself and will do so at the expense of the one that precedes it. Here are two examples:

1) Stomach: the mother is the large intestine; the son is the spleen-pancreas.

The mother: these *p*'s are powerful, strong, demanding.

The son: the rounded part of the letter is clear and well formed, the descending stroke is emphatic and energetic but it returns to the base line.

And here is the stomach, exhausted by a son who takes too much and is suffocated by a mother in full activity.

In conclusion: the writer (a female) is intelligent (*b*'s clearly formed) but her mental rumination (*b*'s filled in) is hampered by too intense a sensitivity (strong *p*'s). Her ideas are clear, but in order to integrate them she must call upon all of her will to structure her work. This constant effort is physically damaging.

2) Kidney: the mother is the bladder; the son is the circulation-sexuality.

The mother; passive, submits — the letter (*n*) has the form of a receptacle.

The son: powerful and in full swing (*j*), is very demanding.

The kidney: this form (*t*) is vague and irregular in appearance — the organ-function suffers.

In conclusion: this writer (a male) suffers from excessive circulation-sexuality. He has demanding sexual needs and satisfies them at the risk of unbalancing his psyche (*n* in the form of a receptacle), and he does not call upon his will to moderate himself. This state of affairs is damaging to his nerves (the kidneys rule the nerves), which are sorely put to the test. In addition to kidney trouble, there is a marked tendency toward depression.

Removal of an Organ

What happens if an organ is removed by surgery? The Chinese say that the function creates the organ. If the latter is eliminated, the function remains and tries to recreate the missing organ. We will present several actual cases so we can understand why this mechanism observed by the Chinese has so much value.

1) Removal of the stomach (Factory of the spleen-pancreas). The patient finds himself with a treasury organ without a factory-organ. Here are the two corresponding letters in his handwriting:

The *b* is that of a function which is indeed handicapped.

This *q* indicates the enormous workload undertaken by the spleen-pancreas (3 knots in the loop), an effort which tires it (return stroke to the base line).

When fatigue becomes too intense and the spleen is too strong (psyche of these two couple organs) the patient regains strength by looking at abstract black and purple paintings.

These sinister colors upset his friends and family, who attribute this activity to his nostalgia and exhaustion. Black is the color of Saturn and this planet rules the spleen; the patient, by immersing himself in black, tries subconsciously to *recreate* his missing factory organ!

2) Removal of the gall bladder in a man. We know that the gall bladder is the factory organ of the liver. But here the liver is alone. What is the liver? It is a Minister of the Chiefs-of-Staff, he elaborates tactics and strategies says Soulié de Morant, and Ch'I-Po replied to the Yellow Emperor that the liver is the Military Chief who excels in strategic planning.[8]

After a hard day's work, this patient (minus his gall bladder) sets up rows of lead soldiers, recreates battles, makes plans. What his family takes to be a harmless eccentricity is in fact his reason for living: he is encouraging his liver organ-function.

3) Removal of the gall bladder in a woman. This woman had wanted to command, organize, and direct all her life. Following suit, her gall bladder filled with wastes and bitterness to such an extent that it had to be removed by surgery. After the operation, the imperative tone decreased, but the liver, left alone, began to encourage the Great Military Chief. Clever plans and stratagems were put into effect to sabotage marriages as soon as she got word of them — or as soon as a project was in the offing. The function tries to recreate the organ.

---

[8]See the *Yellow Emperor*, p. 133.

5

The Four Systems

A letter might well seem a very small thing to contain all by itself such vast issues as characterology and the state of the organs of the human body. However, the study of the four systems[1] will show you that it is not a matter of just one *letter* but of *letters* whose form we will study in accordance with subtle interrelations that are rather far removed from Western concepts, but whose fine Oriental qualities will be readily apparent. These four systems are:

♦ the digestive system (nutrition);
♦ the respiratory system (blood);
♦ the muscular system (energy);
♦ the cerebral system (medulla);

and a fifth one which animates them:

♦ the circulatory system.

Each system has an interior and exterior analyzer that corresponds to a temperament and to a sense, respectively. It affects both the physical and the psychic states.

---

[1]This study is based on a theory proposed by Dr. Choain in *Voie Rationelle de la Médecine Chinoise*, pp. 331 *ff.*

In the following pages you will find detailed tables of the systems, which consist of

$$3 \text{ organ-functions} \begin{cases} 1 \text{ treasury organ} \\ 1 \text{ factory organ} \\ 1 \text{ wife organ} \end{cases}$$

In graphology, the study of the forms of the three letters corresponding to each system will have to be carried out concurrently. A judgment must never be made without a parallel study of the letters according to the role of each organ-function within the system in question.

The Digestive System

Treasury organ: pancreas, q

Wife organ: liver, s, o, l

Factory organ: stomach, b

Psyche: serenity, calm, fulfillment. Obsession, spleen anxiety.

Sense: taste. Accepts or rejects forms = g.

Temperament: lymphatic. Intra and intercellular fluid. Water.

Affects the physical form. Structure of the bones and the flesh. It is a formative system.

The Respiratory System

Treasury organ: lung, h

Wife organ: heart, t (horizontal bar only)

Factory organ: large intestine, p, f

Psyche: self-expansion, self-esteem. Worry.

Sense: the nose, flair, smell. Antenna of sensitivity (sensitivity = intestines).

Temperament: blood. Air. Gas dissolved in the blood.

Affects the vital energy.

The Muscular System

Treasury organ: liver, *s, o, l*

Wife organ: pancreas, *q*

Factory organ: gall bladder, *d*

Psyche: animation, aggressivity. Anger.

Sense: sight, the eyes. Rules the energy of our actions and our work. Good or bad judgment. Discerns or separates forms. Master of the muscles.

Temperament: bile. Fire.

Affects the soul and spiritual faculties.

The Cerebral System

Treasury organ: kidney, *t* (vertical bar only)

Wife organ: circulation-sexuality, *j, e, z*

Factory organ: bladder, *n*

Psyche: concentration, decision. Will. Fear.

Sense: the ears. Divides in half, establishes limits, orients and balances. Master of the nerves.

Temperament: black bile. Earth.

Affects the psychic energy, in relation to will.

The Circulatory System

Treasury organ: heart, *t* (horizontal bar only)

Wife organ: lung, *h*

Factory organ: small intestine, *p, f*

Psyche: the heart is the junction of the four temperaments in the same way as the circulatory system is the soul of the four preceding systems.

Temperament: sensitivity, emotivity, joy.

Affects the psychic energy in general.

Remember that in the study of these systems the treasury organ is of great importance. It gives the keynote to the system to which it belongs. For example, Table 2 shows us how the treasury organs of the system can be studied, without, or course, ever disassociating them from their factories and wives.

You can already understand why the malformed aspects of a *q*, for example, suggest a deficiency of the spleen-pancreas. But this evaluation would be of little value if the examination stopped there.

What is the pancreas in Chinese medicine and what is its role within the various systems? It is a treasury organ within the digestive system and a wife organ within the muscular system. If we know which system is affected, we can determine which part of the psyche is not in harmony. It is therefore necessary to examine the corresponding letters:

Spleen-Pancreas = *q*
Liver = *s, o, l*   } Digestive system
Stomach = *b*

or:

Table 2. The Five Systems.

System	Treasury Organ	Letter	Function
Digestive	Spleen-Pancreas	q	Formation of ideas.
Respiratory	Lungs	h	Formation of the unconscious* of the intelligence of the cells.
Muscular	Liver	s, o, l	Formation of subconscious** of the intelligence of the organs.
Cerebral	Kidneys	v, t (vertical)	Formation of decision.
And the 5th system that animates the others			
Circulatory	Heart	t (horizontal)	Formation of consciousness.

*State wherein consciousness is absent.

**State in which consciousness is on hold (threshold state).

$$\left.\begin{array}{l} \text{Liver} = s,\ o,\ l \\ \text{Spleen-Pancreas} = q \\ \text{Gall Bladder} = d \end{array}\right\} \quad \text{Muscular system}$$

Rarely does only one organ-function break down in a given system: the unhealthy state of one inevitably entails the dysfunction of the others. It is easier to discover which system is defective than we might think. However, lest the joy of discovery fill us with too much pride, remember the game of pick-up-sticks, and think of the great care with which we must examine a specimen of handwriting in order to avoid making mistakes.

And do not think that our work stops there! Having located the defective system, we must study each of its organ-functions in turn so as to grasp fully the significance of each and to understand which is at fault in the triangle, why it has gone awry, and how to put it back on its way to good physical and psychic health. Here are two graphological examples:

Cerebral System

Treasury = Kidney t (vertical bar), and v;
Factory = Bladder n;
Wife = Circulation-Sexuality j, e, z;

$\mathcal{C}$

The v's have the appearance of an o, almost totally closed. There is a tyrannical treasury-organ (o = Tower of the Tarot, symbol of egotism and pride) whose decisions are all that matters. It is a barrier that allows nothing to filter through and whose concentration is excessive.

L

This sketchy n, without a beginning or an end, is symbolic of a factory bladder that is exhausted and atrophied.

$\checkmark$

The e's are also sketchy and incomplete, as are the n's of the bladder. The j's are above the base line and seem to be "out of the running."

In conclusion: by an excess of will and concentration, the kidney treasury-organ paralyzes the bladder and the circulation-sexuality by submitting them exclusively to its decisions. It drains everything away like a Dictator. And just as the ear knows how to tune out whatever it does not want to hear, this writer knows how to turn a deaf ear to everything that does not correspond to her desires.

Physically, circulation-sexuality is disrupted and this disfunction manifests itself each month by a flow of blood into the kidneys (which drain everything). This blood is evacuated by the bladder. Psychologically, this is the sort of woman who has a tendency to take on the man's role, either because she unconsciously regrets not being one (she deviates her menstruation from its normal channels, but menstruates nonetheless), or because of the demands of her life.

The mind, by the force of its own will, directs, wills, concentrates, orders. The influence of others counts for naught: he hears who wants to hear. Graphologically, this is a purely psychological case that will improve and re-balance itself only when the writer becomes conscious of her state (of being).

Respiratory System

Treasury = Lungs *h*.
Factory = Large Intestine *p*.
Wife = Heart *t* (horizontal bar).

This malformed *h* has a clear but small loop with a blocked lower arcade which indicates a treasury organ in a deficient state.

The *p* suffers from this bad system of oxygen entry and exit and it in turn holds in. The intestines are constipated.

The *t* bar buckles under too heavy a load. It is an exhausted wife-organ, but which manages to maintain its balance nonetheless (note the length of either side is the same).

In conclusion: the respiratory system affects the vital energy. Here it is restrained, and the writer, in order to survive, tries to ease matters by living at a reduced pace (the slow rhythm of the handwriting confirms this fact). Only the heart keeps its balance, but it needs to be treated gently.

Psychologically, the writer is conscious of his heart condition: he therefore gives only the minimum of himself. This is a typical example of egotism out of necessity.

6

The Digestive Cycle

The digestive cycle involves three movements in three phases.[1]

    1) ENTRY   - Absorption   - Sensation

    2) CROSSING   - Interrelation   - Consciousness

    3) EXIT   - Elimination   - Action

Each of the three movements of this cycle represents the work done by:

♦ two treasury organs that deal with energy;

♦ two factory organs that deal with form and matter.

Thus, we have four coupled organ-functions, with their energy coordinated, each one being equal in strength. In each movement:

♦ a treasury organ-function and a factory organ-function play an active role: they are the *Governors*;

---

[1]This digestive cycle, which is interesting for its graphological correspondences, is based on the theories of Dr. Choain in *Voie Rationelle de la Medecine Chinoise*, pp. 208 *ff*.

♦ a treasury organ-function and a factory organ-function play a passive role: they are *Governed*.

We notice that one treasury is active while the other is passive; it is the same thing with the factories. Why? Because the principle of couple organs is one of harmony and balance: it is not attached to a specific organ-function, but to the role that these organ-functions play in relation to one another within the cycle.

If we consider the first movement of absorption, we find that the absorption of energy is carried out by the lungs and heart treasury organs. They are both passive organs, but compared to one another the lungs are active, regulatory, and so governors; the heart is passive, submissive, and so governed.

As mentioned at the end of chapter 1, this Chinese concept is also to be found in Western philosophy. It enables us to understand Table 3 regarding the entire digestive system.

Table 3. Outline of a Digestive Cycle.

Movement	Treasuries	Factory
Absorption	Lungs	+ Large Intestine = coupled governing organs
Sensation	Heart	+ Small Intestine = coupled governed organs
Interrelation	Spleen Pancreas	+ Stomach = coupled governing organs
Consciousness	Liver	+ Gall Bladder = coupled governed organs
Elimination	Circulation Sexuality	+ Triple Heater = coupled governing organs
Action	Kidney	+ Bladder = coupled governed organs

1st Movement: Absorption

In its literal sense, the verb *to absorb* means the penetration of a solid, liquid, or gaseous element from the exterior to the interior. Psychologically, it is the absorption of the outer environment by the subject, an absorption producing a sensation of acceptance or of rejection. This movement is satisfying in itself when it functions harmoniously, if not, it causes worry and sorrow.

This cycle corresponds to the four organ-functions: lung and its factory, the large intestine (*h* and *p, f*). And to heart and its factory of small intestine (*t* horizontal bar, and *p, f*).

This movement corresponds psychically to feeling ("sensation" in French) and takes place in two parts:

Absorption of Energy

By the two treasury organs (the lungs and the heart), which here are governor and governed, that is to say, in harmony.

Plato, in the *Timaeus*, explains the cycle of respiration and circulation by comparing the lungs to a sponge which, placed around the heart, refreshes it from the fire that keeps burning it. Chinese medicine shows the importance of a harmonious balance of the heart-lung rhythm. The heart allows the outer environment of oxygen energy to penetrate into the inner environment. Psychologically, at issue is the reaction of the individual in the face of the *unknown*.

It is said that the sense of smell and "flair" represent the mouth of the lungs. If the individual has been well guided by his flair, the reaction is healthy and there is calm, but if his flair has been faulty, what comes into play? The heart. We have often noticed that under the influence of a strong emotion "one suffocates and the heart beats so strongly that it seems as if it were about to burst." This is a matter of the inner reaction in relation to the outer action.

Lungs and heart are therefore linked as the two aspects of the absorption of energy. And we can already guess that a heart which beats badly, but which is connected to healthy lungs, can allow the individual to live. On another level, it is the governed suffocated by the governor. For the one there is worry, and for the other, self-esteem.

Material Absorption

By the two factory organs — the large and the small intestines. The large and small intestine are the two aspects of material absorption. They allow entry of the outer material environment into the inner environment, in the circulatory current in reaction to the pulmonary activity. They represent a reaction of the organism to the outer environment, the absorption of substances. These two organs are yang, they are factory-organs whose husband-wife principle reflect harmony.

Psychologically, the intestines represent sensitivity, all that is hidden and private in the person, that which takes place in darkness. It is the process of feeling. In the same way that the large intestine holds on to or throws out non-useable waste matter, sensitivity holds on to or rejects forms after having "absorbed" them.

This state — Absorption (g) — therefore implies a choice. The subjective reflection is hunger or affectivity as feeling (sensation).

The Buddhist idea of hunger is that it gives rise to desire which generates action (the Hebrew letter GIMEL is an open hand which takes). A g letter form which does not follow the classical type, as is often the case, must immediately be noted, but before coming to any conclusion, this letter must be studied in conjunction with the form of the letters of the entire cycle, that is, the letters h, t (horizontal bar), p, and f.

This well-traced letter, though it has a prominent loop, indicates someone who is hungry and who likes to eat: it is a materialistic hunger.

This *g* has a lower loop in the shape of a triangle. It is the form of the reed scepter of the Egyptians and it corresponds to the letter YOD. It represents Self-realization: this is someone who feels great satisfaction in eating well, which gives the impression of having realized himself or herself. This action of absorption is often seen in emotive and sensual types.

This *g*, in simplified spiral form, symbolizes speed. Its outline reminds one of an *s* and this letter corresponds to SHIN, which represents fire. On the physical level, there is a lack of appetite (the fire dies out); but on the psychological level, it is an indication of very rapid comprehension, sharp impressions of all that is exterior to, and which surrounds the person here, all sensation of ideas takes place at lightning speed.

If, with this form of *g*, the *p*'s and the *f*'s are defective, one must conclude that the "sorting" in the selection of ideas takes place through the sensitivity in absorbing ideas (sensitivity = intestines). These factories suffer and the vital energy is affected by this.

Here the body of the letter is sketchy, but the lower loop is normal: this indicates a tendency toward anorexia and also a filtering of the entrance of ideas, which does not necessarily mean that there is discernment!

Here is a *g* whose twisted and eccentric form rests above the line, the lower loop is on the same level as the *o*'s and the *a*'s of the text, the upper loop being in the air. This is a mentality that refuses to absorb external ideas and that desires to maintain its intimate self intact to protect it jealously against any intrusions from without. On the physical level, the repercussions generally take place in the second cycle of interrelation. We will study this later, but keep in mind that the vulnerable point is the stomach.

This letter has a very large stomach which will overlap with the letters on the next line. It gives preference to all material absorption: we have often seen it among those who abuse alcohol.

Following is an example where the *g* sums up well the four letters of this movement. In a handwriting sample we found:

h — this letter presents an irregular form throughout the text.

t — same comment as above.

p — this letter indicates great strength, since it clearly towers above the other letters in the handwriting.

Thus an irregular governor (lungs) and a strong governor (large intestine); an irregular governed (heart) and a strong governed (small intestine).

The form of the *g* confirms that this idea, for in an interval of three lines we can find two completely different variations.

In conclusion: in all of the aspects concerning this first movement of the digestive cycle, the writer is *manic-depressive* in relation to:

1) his nutritional absorption;

2) the power of his vital energy;

3) the sensations exposed to his sensitivity;

4) his defense before the unknown;

5) his self-satisfaction. But here, by the form of the
   a's[2] which are large, strong, and definite, we can
   state that the writer, is rather satisfied with himself in spite of this manic-depression.

2nd Movement: Interrelation

This second stage of material exchange involves the spleen-
pancreas and its factory the stomach (q and b), the liver and
its factory, the gall bladder (s, o, l and d). This movement,
which has its psychic correspondence in consciousness, works
in two phases.

Fixation Functions

By way of the two spleen-pancreas and liver treasuries, the
inner environment accepts the outer environment. It is assimilation in the material form that builds. It is the energy of the
Chinese. Psychologically, we are dealing with an elementary
consciousness that builds concepts (mental forms). These
functions bring about phlegm (serenity or spleen).

Transformatory Functions

Through the two factories of the stomach and the gall bladder, the inner environment transforms the outer environment. It is disassimilation — energy that destroys through
movement.

Psychologically, it is basic consciousness that sets its
concepts in motion by means of reasoning (mental energy).
These functions bring about animation or aggressivity.

Let me mention here the very important role of the factories: *the stomach* (b), whose activity directs material inte-

---

[2]The a will be studied in the next chapter.

gration. It transforms, analyzes, makes assimilable the spleen-pancreas through its treasury.

The gall bladder directs the integration of energy — the flow of bile over the nutrients from the outside world, decomposes it, and makes it assimilable by way of its treasury, the liver. There is no letter which graphologically sums up this second stage as the letter *g* did for the first stage.

We are dealing here not with one action, that of swallowing followed by sensation; we have four organ functions that work to assimilate what they have been given.

In order to understand how this cycle is manifested in the handwriting, we must examine the letters that correspond to the four organ-functions by bringing into play the correspondences of fixation or transformation of this assimilation.

The following example shows how this second stage can be studied:

The *q*'s are of a normal size, but with a very inclined and stressed lower stroke, and a return stroke that connects with the following letter from the bottom (an unnecessary movement).

Open *o*, loose but no knots.

Fine *b*'s, well defined, detached from the preceding letter. They are independent.

The *d*'s, in the form of a musical note, with a curved descending stroke that is detached and heavily drawn.

When we analyze this we find that the spleen-pancreas (*q*) functions defectively; it connects with the following letter from the bottom. It is therefore anemic. Its stressed lower loop indicates overstimation of the self. This anemia leads to spleen.

The liver (*s, o, l*) is weak. The governed opens itself too much, it is passive and accepts all that befalls it without rancor. No excess of bile — the *o*'s are clear. The *s*'s and the *l*'s confirm this point of view. The governed lacks self-esteem: it is dominated by the governor and opens itself out of self-protection.

The stomach factory (*b*) is running well. But it does so alone (the letter is not attached to the preceding one) and it strives to function vigorously. If there is spleen through the spleen-pancreas, there is nonetheless no trace of psychic anxiety (the specialty of the stomach).

The gall bladder factory (*d*) is running well also. In this handwriting, it is the two treasuries that are weak. However, in this cycle it is the two treasuries that create the physical condition: the subject is anemic, with a tendency toward weakness which makes him prone to "far niente" (do nothing), to daydreaming without goal or purpose.

To look at this from a psychological point of view, these two treasury-organs indicate the personal relationship of the subject relative to the external environment. There is acceptance in spite of themselves — of intrusion from the outside.

There is neither bitterness, rebellion, nor animosity (gall bladder): there is spleen and nostalgia and a marked desire for solitude. Why? The answer comes from its two factories:

BETH (the letter corresponding to the stomach, *b*) is the spiritual letter that seeks evolution; the subject seeks alone (*b*, isolated) and seeks a lot (*b*, large and clearly defined). DALETH (gall bladder, *d*) is the one that receives from the cosmos and here it is receptive to the vibrations received.

This handwriting is representative of a loner who wants to search alone and in peace along the path. He pays for this solitude with physical weakness, for if one gives to others, others will give in return in an incessant exchange, and he who does not submit to this law of balance will have to pay the price.

3rd Movement: Elimination

Elimination is the rejection, the expulsion, by the organism, of certain substances drawn from the inner environment toward the outer environment. It is the division of the environment into the inside and the outside. It is the source of the motives for action in the Buddhist sense. In psychology it is *decision* (decision = separation of ego from non-ego).

This third movement is accomplished by the two organ-functions. The kidneys and their factory, the bladder (*t*, vertical bar), *v*, and *n*. Nothing is lost, nothing is gained. All is one by a continuous movement of circulating energy. The Chinese know this well, and at the point of this third movement which ought to close the digestive cycle, they show that nothing ends but that all continues through the two functions of the circulation-sexuality (*j, e, z*) and its factory, the triple heater (*v*).

If the kidney-bladder couple, by condensing and eliminating, is the guardian of the balance of health (structured by the spleen-pancreas during the 2nd movement of the cycle), the circulation-sexuality and triple heater couple comes to eliminate by the power of its energy, not to conserve but to produce: for to create is to die.[3]

This third stage is that of action, of decision and of the separation of the ego from the non-ego. We will present an example of what can be done in graphology by the examination of this third movement.

The *j* and *e* are very well formed. The circulation-sexuality function is at full steam and suffers no ill effects.

The *v*'s of the triple-heater are neat, precise, very well formed and always detached from the text. It is a yang force that is very well "called up" and very well "received." It is in vibration.

The *t*'s of the kidneys have irregular forms. They are most often written with weak (as in the sample) or missing parts, but the latter only intermittently, for in the same text we find excellent and very well-defined *t*'s. It is a kidney barrier that holds, but which could also give way in the event of a great shock.

The *n*'s of the bladder are supple, disciplined, and give the impression of unimpaired functioning.

---

[3]From which we can see the primitive connection between the sexual and urinary processes.

In conclusion: this handwriting is that of an individual of action, whose activity is strong and constant. But when the rate of energy becomes too great, the overload breaks the barrier of the kidneys. They receive a physical shock and suffer the consequences in the form of pain. Psychologically, in this handwriting the will to action sometimes surpasses energy potential and so the nerves (masters of the kidneys) break down: the consequences are acute indecisiveness and difficulty in concentrating (psyche of the kidneys).

On the other hand, if the kidneys and the bladder suffer the backlash of the hyperactivity, it should be noted that it never affects the circulation-sexuality/triple heater couple. A curious and paradoxical thing is that, graphologically, we must conclude that this governing couple of the 3rd cycle, which is solely responsible for the temporary breakdown of their governed, by the same enormous force which unbalanced them, re-balances them through fresh supplies. Activity is thus resumed, and the nerves hold, until the next assault and another temporary collapse!

7

The Spiritual Path

Three letters of the alphabet have not yet been clearly defined in this book. They are ALEPH (*a*), MEM (*m*), and SHIN (*s*). I have not forgotten them, nor put them aside intentionally. According to ancient teachings, these three Mother letters[1] have no astrological correspondences and are not involved medically since no organs are attributed to them.

I would not pursue these explanations any further if readers were not already on the path that leads to the study of the being in its triple aspect of body, soul, and spirit. Medicine has helped us to study the body, and psychology and the psyche to study the soul.

We will now take a glimpse at the spirit thanks to the three Mother letters. I say glimpse because — like a flash of lightning during a storm — the spirit cannot be seen, or heard, or understood in its true essence. It is a part of the All, it is the unknowable, it is That which allows us to unite with That which Is. But, before reaching this goal, we must take the step of renouncing the ego in order to accede to the superior Self which, by means of wisdom, unites with universal consciousness.

---

[1]In the Hebraic alphabet, there are 3 Mother letters, 7 Double letters, and 12 Simple letters.

This is what is known, in the West, as treading the path of knowledge, and in the Orient, as being enlightened. Nor is this in contradiction with the teachings of the Catholic Church, according to which one must "reach heaven to attain sainthood."

If we, by means of spirit, take a path to attain a spiritual goal, it is undeniable that the vibrations received from the subtle centers which we cross will have repercussions upon the body and soul, since body, soul, and spirit are one; and this is why this chapter was written.

To continue with the terminology used throughout this book, let's say that:

 ALEPH (*a*) corresponds to the magician and to the first steps along the spiritual path (1st major arcanum of the tarot).

 MEM (*m*) corresponds to the reaper which brings renewal through death (13th major arcanum).

SHIN (*s*) corresponds to the fool which is the attainment of wisdom — or madness (22nd major arcanum).

Using the symbol of the tulip, the flower of initiation,[2] the tarot shows a closed one at the feet of the magician, and one in full bloom at the feet of the fool. This means that at the beginning of the path, knowledge is in a state of hope and promise, and the trials of transformation imposed by the reaper will show if the initiation is to be continued or stopped. Only those who can overcome the 21st arcanum of the World (Rota) will be granted the blooming tulip of the 22nd arcanum. The spirit, through initiation, will have completed its cycle, having transcended the ego and reached the Self through wisdom.

Along the ascent, the rungs of the ladder are infinite and the way to climb them is specific to each individual. Many reach the first levels and do not continue, proud of the feeling of peace they have found there, thinking that they have reached the summit. Others (forgetting the symbol of Jacob who, having done everything in his physical power, fell asleep at the foot of the ladder while the Angels ascended and descended for him), want to be the conquerors of this knowledge.

To illustrate this, let's discuss, in graphological terms, three states of being along the path by studying together the three Mother letters *a, m,* and *s.* These are the three journeys

---

[2]In the Orient, this symbol is the lotus.

that the writers were in the midst of when they wrote the samples you will see. The changes of direction that they took in their lives will be reflected through changes in the forms of these three letters.

Here is the first episode along the path:

$$\mathcal{A} = \text{"}a\text{"} \qquad \mathcal{M} = \text{"}m\text{"} \qquad \mathcal{P} = \text{"}s\text{"}$$

ALEPH: The Aleph is yang, full of sun and Light. Its symbol is the eagle.[3] This letter corresponds to the sun and symbolizes the vital force that pierces the shadows by means of the light which it emits. It is reason which makes us the image of God by elevating us above all created beings.

From the outset this *a*, the object of our study, presents a closed corner, an obscure, shadowy triangle that cuts off the roundness of the letter. The sun cannot shine forth if part of it is obstructed by a cloud. The Magician (the arcanum corresponding to this letter) who sets off on the path in this way has not totally given himself over to the Light, he has set aside for himself a small plot, a sort of store for provisions. We will see how this self-preservation will prevent him from going further along the path; the balloon will not go far if we do not play out the string.

MEM = the Mem is yin and reflects death. Its symbol is the vulture and solitude. It is at night and in inner silence that we can meditate in order to liberate ourselves. Death is a renewal.

In connection with this initiatory mystery, the Egyptians celebrated a rite for the Pharaohs and the Head Priests, a ceremony called "The Crossing by the Skin." There were three skins and they symbolized the Death of the Initiate and his rebirth into a new state. If the three legs of the *m* are symbols of the three skins, then we can see here that the

---

[3]The Egyptian hieroglyph for Aleph is an eagle.

passage has not been made — the knots bind the MEM and do not liberate it.

SHIN = the shin symbolizes the rising flame, singing the joy of the spirit that has overcome all obstacles and liberated itself, allowing the lotus to bloom. The graphological image which this SHIN shows us is striking: there is a dome and not a flame nor a lotus in bloom. This *s*, which is like a well-sealed skull cap, says much about the one who is advancing along the path. The Fool has attained neither wisdom nor madness. He is still only a magician.

In the second episode:

$$\mathcal{el} = \text{"}a\text{"} \qquad \mathcal{lll} = \text{"}m\text{"} \qquad \wedge = \text{"}s\text{"}$$

ALEPH = this magician sets off with very definite premises — a sense of her femininity and of ego: the writer starts her *a* with an *e*.

In fact, the HÉ (*e*) corresponds to circulation-sexuality in its passive, static feminine form, which awaits the stimulus of YOD to give it life. Thus, in her momentum along the path, this magician has placed all that she considered as most precious in herself, that being her fertilized feminine nature. It was a false start, at her first attempt to ascend, she encounters an obstacle and immediately reverses gears. The current of the circulation of energy ran into a barrier in its very first attempts at ascension.

The solar plexus *a* is not made to receive (the HÉ is a cup), it is made to give light.

MEM = if the Aleph has turned its back on yang, the MEM has done the same toward the yin. This is further proof that although this person is seeking to evolve, she is going about it backward.

SHIN = In fact, the Shin becomes YOD because of its rectilinear form, and, in her text, when there are two *s*'s side by side, they look like a NUN (*n*). The YOD, like the NUN, is a sign of virility and action. They animate the HÉ, but this is

not the right way to go about it. We therefore conclude that
this young woman has taken a path to nowhere. From the
beginning, not feeling a sure footing on the path (and rightly
so), she tried through the SHIN to reverse the roles and to
take hold of knowledge, to conquer it by every possible
means. And the form of her *s*'s hint that she in fact seeks
power through knowledge—the complete opening at the
baseline indicates a materialistic and yin orientation. In the
third episode:

$$\mathcal{U} = "a" \qquad \mathcal{M} = "m" \qquad \int = "s"$$

ALEPH = This Aleph begins like an *l* and then, with a
graceful curve, extends a hand to the following letter. A sun
which gives of itself (LAMED) without hesitation (no
hooks), without any reserve (the letter is pure), is the kind of
magician who from his first steps on the path has known how
to find the TAO.

MEM = "The Passage by the Skin" has left this magician pure and transparent. No hate, no regret, no unnecessary strokes. The MEM has made its harvest and left the
Being with its essence to permit it to live. The initiation into
the arcanum was passed with flying colors.

SHIN = And the Shin was attained in a single movement. The serpent has raised its head; the tulip has bloomed;
the fool has found wisdom.

8

Anguish

To give an idea of what can be learned through judicious use of the psychology of the organs according to the Chinese tradition as applied to graphology, we will use an issue of great concern today as an example. Anguish is one of our biggest problems — along with the phenomena that it entails.

What is anguish? This word comes from the Latin *angustia*, which means constriction; it can be of a physical, moral, or psychic order. Anguish gives the sensation of an undefinable dis-ease which overwhelms us like mist settling on a field at sundown.

This sensation is a psychic phenomenon that originates in the first digestive cycle of absorption[1] and which is created by the following organ-functions:

♦ the lungs and their factory, the large intestine;

♦ the heart and its factory, the small intestine.

As a result of emotional upsets, of which we are not always conscious, the sensitivity of the intestines alerts their treasuries, the lungs and the heart. The cardio-pulmonary

---

[1]See chapter 6.

system thus comes into play (this warning can be experienced in sensitive people as pain in the corresponding vertebrae).

The lungs form the unconscious and the intelligence of the cells. They rule the heart, which forms the consciousness. It is the heart which is affected first, or at least which, through consciousness, calls attention to itself by accelerated heartbeats (or by a slowing down of its rhythm) and feelings of anguish (emotive sensitivity). In graphology it is the *p*'s and the horizontal bars of the *t*'s that are affected.

Only the lungs, the governors of this cycle, can restore balance through calm and well-paced breathing, for they rule over the intelligence of the cells of which we are not conscious. The *h*'s need to be full in order to forestall anguish. In any case, our vital energy is affected: to dispel the anguish requires an energy which few possess, and it is therefore diminished.

If the lungs, a treasury organ, do not re-establish the normal rhythm, this sensation becomes more and more accentuated, it settles in and reaches the second cycle, which is that of consciousness.

This second cycle is realized by the spleen-pancreas and its factory, the stomach; and the liver, and its factory, the gall bladder. The spleen-pancreas forms the ideas. When there is anguish, the ideas are no longer clearly formed; they are troubled and the liver as treasury organ, underassisted, falls out of harmony.

Now, the liver forms the subconscious and the intelligence of the organs. In graphology it is the *q*'s, the *s*'s, *o*'s, and the *l*'s that will have malformations.

Up to this point, the irritation, the despair, or the languor was only mental; but at the level of the second cycle, the stomach, a governing factory, physically takes hold and we suffer from cramps (purely of a psychic nature) which can even lead to ulcers. The *b*'s open themselves to the yin (for details on this letter see the chapter on the organ-function of the stomach) and the anguish, having found its source, gives no respite.

The vital energy, already greatly diminished by the malfunctioning of the first cycle, is now incapable of maintaining the physical condition, the structure of the bones and of the flesh (psyche of the digestive system whose factory is the stomach). I know of cases of nervous depression which, having developed to the point of affecting the stomach, led not only to a noticeable decrease in physical strength, but also to bone fractures in the legs and a deterioration of the skin, which became rough and unwholesome.

The fourth organ function of the cycle, the gall bladder, plays an important role relative to the effects of anguish at this stage. It is the factory organ in relation to the cosmos by way of the triple heater. If it resists the invasion of aggressness or anger, it is because it is like an emperor who remains unperturbed in the midst of torment, and who can therefore prevent the poison from doing its work. It is those who enable the spiritual faculties (psyche of the muscular system of which the gall bladder is the factory) that restore order.

The *d*'s are indicative of a pro or con reaction toward the invasion of anguish and to its take-over of the subject. If the *d*'s are normal and well-drawn, then the gall bladder is holding up: the anguish can be cured. If they are badly written, the nervous breakdown could push the writer to suicide. By badly written we mean weak and without consistency. We must then turn to the form of the *b*'s.

In the case of a possible suicide, this letter, in addition to an opening toward the yin, has a bar at the top, as if to cut off all contact with life (BETH = evolution). We will study this situation at the end of this chapter.

When anguish has penetrated the individual to this level of consciousness, the patient tries in every possible way, and especially by instinct, to reach the third cycle: to effect the elimination of this anguish.

The third cycle, elimination, is assured by circulation-sexuality and its factory, the triple heater; and the kidney and its factory, the bladder.

Evolved people who have let themselves be taken over insidiously will eliminate the anguish by calling upon the triple heater factory which, by its influx of yang from the cosmos, will provide circulation-sexuality with heat and life. This current will enable them to reestablish spiritual — as well as physical and emotional — equilibrium; the anguish will dissipate like smoke. The $v, j, e,$ and z will reflect this.

However, unevolved people with a defective gall bladder will not be able to call upon the triple heater, which is unable to act if its reflective mirror is out of action: these people will therefore try to eliminate anguish by the governed of the third cycle, the kidneys and the bladder. They will turn to material and sensual means, such as the use of tobacco, narcotics, drink, excessive sex, etc.. How much vice and abuse has no other origin than this!

At the third cycle level, the nerves (master of the kidneys) are shaken and we find acute nervous depression. Stop-gap stimulants over-excite the factory organs and, far from restoring balance, attack the circulation-sexuality treasury organ: which itself no longer functions, no longer emits, and, since it is not seconded by its teammate, the triple heater, it can no longer govern. The latter then becomes a radar without a receptive "head." As for the tranquilizing expedients, they put everything to sleep, and it is no longer question of a "consciousness that seeks to eliminate." It is to this consciousness that we have to answer upon awakening, at the risk of being faced sooner or later with the same situation.

People at this stage of the third cycle of elimination are in the grips of a sensuality that the nerves can no longer control, a state in which fear and over-decisiveness alternate and overwhelm, while they feel caught in a vicious circle with no way out. The psychic energy is chaotic. Anguish that has become nervous depression turns into despair.

Modern medicine invented electroshock therapy and this coincides with the Chinese medical point of view that attributes to the mental system the role played by the kidney-bladder circulation-sexuality. Indeed, those who can no longer receive cosmic vibrations (which are electrical vibrations) with the triple heater sometimes regain equilibrium thanks to the electrical impulses from these mechanical substitutes.

Serenity and calm are the lot of those who rule over a universe where we tend our own role and not to that of our neighbor, where there is neither covetousness nor laziness. Anguish has no place in the realm of balance and harmony, it cannot establish itself there. If by chance it should get its foot in the door, it can be chased away by conscious deep and measured breathing. If this is not done, the process described above will go into operation.

The following is a sample of one man's handwriting that passed through all the various stages of anguish and ended in suicide. We will study in turn the forms of the letters corresponding to the three cycles.

1st Cycle: Sensation

The lungs (*h*) no longer breathe properly. Their absorption is unruly, eccentric, and gives a feeling of imbalance. The lungs form the intelligence of the cells. Here there is perfect disorder.

The heart (*t*) indicates uneven and haphazard heartbeats. None of the *t* bars are in their proper places! Consciousness has been warned that something is not going right.

$$\mathcal{V}$$

The intestines (p) are completely indistinct. The sensitivity has been affected and suffers. The sensation of anguish is permanent. Has it reached consciousness?

2nd Cycle: Consciousness

$$\gamma$$

The spleen-pancreas, q, is healthy and in good condition. It is the organ that forms the ideas. And here they are sharp and clear. Anguish has not troubled them. It is an unaltered treasury which is the only unsapped pillar in the physical edifice.

$$\mathcal{l}$$

The liver (l) is malfunctioning. The l's are irregular and confused in form. The o's are reduced to small vertical strokes without any curves. The liver forms the intelligence of the organs. We can say that here the organs, like the cells, are hardly directed. The liver is also the tone of the organism. The form of this l says it all.

The d's of the gall bladder have a strange form. They first take on the form of a clear, neat, and harmonious mirror (in the shape of a musical note), then, as if by a sudden decision by the writer, the mirror is obstructed with a loop which does not belong there and which makes an *l*, letter of sacrifice.

The *b* of the stomach has a bar which blocks the evolution and prevents the individual from lifting his head up to the heavens. Through a sharp movement toward the baseline this lance will terminate life (life is the base line).

Anguish has now reached the state of nervous depression with thoughts of suicide. Will the writer be able to eliminate it? Only the ideas are clear, a momentary lapse into sensual abuse will suffice for him to forget. His ideas will become blocked, and no longer the master of his ship, he could resort to the irreparable. Let us look at the third cycle.

3rd Cycle: Elimination

The circulation-sexuality with its *j*'s is reduced to its simplest expression. It exists as a treasury, but does it really live? The *e*'s in the text are practically non-existent.

As for the *i*'s (*i* and *j* = YOD), they present a very bizarre appearance when preceded by a *b*.

As you can see in the illustration, the despairing morbidity of the individual (betrayed by the descending bar of the *b*) does not even find satisfaction in sexuality, and if we accept that YOD represents the individual, we can only be struck by the connecting of these letters.

The vertical line of the *t*'s hover above the base line. The kidneys are floating, their decisiveness is inoperative and goes along according to the whim of the impulses.

This *n* shows that the bladder does what it can. It seems irritated by the lack of harmony and continuity to which it is subjected by the kidneys. It is a "picky" factory which submits because it has no choice, but it eliminates badly.

There is every reason to believe that the writer does not eliminate his anguish. Only the triple heater remains to be examined in this last cycle. The door at which the triple heater is knocking (assuming that it is functioning) will not open, since the obstructed gall bladder cannot receive its vibrations. No salvation can come from there.

And what about vice? Look at sensuality (*j*) and absorption (*g*). In this handwriting, they are written in the form of passageways by means of vertical strokes. Everything slides off, nothing can reach this person — except the despair which is eating away at him. Certainly at this stage, if not before, professional counseling is strongly recommended. To his way of thinking, suicide seemed to be the only way out.

9

Key Words and Case Histories

There are a number of concepts that have been discussed in the text in regard to both physical and psychological health as we can diagnose it through the formation of letters. This chapter includes a list of key words that can help students grasp the words that are associated with psychological states and certain letter forms. Several case histories have also been included so that students can familiarize themselves all the more with the graphological approach discussed in this book.

Key Words

The following key words are some of the correspondences that we have been able to establish between psychology and the letters of the alphabet, according to the traditional teachings. This is only a first synthesis and its value will always hinge on this principle: *Letters must not be judged individually but always in relation to other letters.*

Aggressivity,   through lack of balance = *h*
                                 through bitterness = *t*
                                 through disgust = *s, o, l*

Ambition,   through desire for conquest = t
                   through desire for accumulation = q, d

Anger,   through aggression = s, o, l
                   through reaction of the nerves = t, v
                   through need to dominate = d

Authority,   through intelligence = d
                   through will = t, v
                   through desire for justice = h

Belligerence,   through a desire for authority = h
                   through a gift for leadership = d

Concentration,   mental = v, t
                   through meditation, rumination = b
                   through love of plans = s, o, l

Consciousness,   formation = t

Courage, d

Death and
its problems, o, m

Decisiveness,   through concentration = v, t, n
                   through will = d

Discernment,   through intelligence = t, e, q
                   through clarity of sight = d
                   through lucidness = s, o, l
                   through balance = h

Emotion,   through feelings = p
                   through affectivity = t
                   through human contact = h
                   as sensation = g

Fear, v, t

Finances,   administration = p, f
                   desire to accumulate = s, p
                   balance = h
                   organization = q

Flair,

through know-how = h
through sensitivity = p
through clairvoyance = s, o, l
through sensation = g

Health,

b

Ideas,

formation = q
absorption = g
assimilation and analysis = b

Intelligence,

of the heart = t
sexual = j, e, z
of ideas = q
of the soul = b
of the organs = s, o, l
of the cells = h

Judgment,

through discernment = s, o, l
through inner rectitude = d

Lazyness,

through fatigue = o

Magnetism,

p, f

Memory,

b

Music,

t, v

Nerves,

t, v

Organization,

social = h
of ideas = l

Pride,

h, t, v

Psyche,

balance = b, v, t, r, d
psychic anguish = b
spleen or serenity = q
clairvoyance = s, o, l
mental energy = b, d
psychic energy = n, p, f
psychic courage = d

Reasoning,	wisdom = *b*
	through plans, strategies = *s, o, l*
	mental conceptualization = *j, e, z*
	concepts = *b, d*
Secretiveness,	sense of the secretive = *s*
	false, base = *o*
Selfishness,	*s, o, l*
Selflessness,	*l*
Sensitivity,	affective = *p*
	feeling = *t, h*
	sensation = *g*
Sexuality,	mental = *j, e, z*
	through magic currents = *s*
	material = *c*
	energy = *s*
Sociability,	contact with superiors and inferiors = *h*
	acceptance or refusal
	of human contact = *b*
	reaction before the unknown = *h, t*
Sympathy,	*t*
Talkativeness,	through sexual repression, *j, e, z*
	through sociability = *h*
	through ease of expression = *p, r*
Understanding,	from the heart = *t*
Vital energy,	its strength = *h*
	its source = *b*
	its tone = *s, o, l*
	its warmth = *a*
	its reserve = *q*
	in the area of work = *p*
Will,	imperative, energetic = *d*
	gentle and patient = *e*
	firm but gentle, that of the leader = *v*

Case Histories

We have included a number of examples. None of the readings are conclusive; the examples show students what can be seen in the handwriting. Some samples are in English, some in French, and the different languages should also indicate how to read various kinds of the handwriting. To grasp the essence of the personality and have it come to life, it is necessary for a graphological study to be done with insight and depth.

The student needs to look at a handwriting specimen without getting lost in the content of the words, much in the same way that we can contemplate a landscape without knowing the name of the locale but only its topology.

First, we look at the writing overall, and then return to those letters of the alphabet which stand out because of one feature or another. This, of course, is not to say that an unusual letterform is representative of something negative, but rather of characteristics and individualistic traits.

Work of this nature requires a certain degree of humility and sincerity, as well as respect for the other without letting that create the fear of seeing another's weaknesses. In fact, many weaknesses – when given a different orientation – can well be considered desirable qualities. An overly inquisitive person has what it takes to be a good detective; a compulsive organizer could become a productive manager, and so on.

None of the following analyses are to be considered as exhaustive; instead they are intended to show only the most striking details of each personality. Keep in mind also that a graphological analysis is like an X-ray taken on a given day – it is not necessarily representative of the situation of an entire lifetime.

Handwriting Sample 1

Cher Monsieur.

C'est avec regret que nous avons eu connaissance de votre décision de nous quitter.

Nous comprenons très bien les motifs qui vous animent pour autant que votre opinion vous intéresse, nous vous donnons entièrement raison.

Dear Sir,

It is with regret that we were informed of your decision to leave us.

We will understand the reasons which motivate you, inasmuch as you respect our point of view we recognize that you are right.

• • •

The handwriting is not shaky but written with firmness. The full orbit of the capital *c*'s indicates physical robustness; this woman also enjoys a hearty meal — notice the strength in the letter *g* (second line: "regret"). And she is 80 years old!

Opinionated, persevering, she writes along a solid baseline, almost as if she were following imaginary ruled lines. And thus well grounded, with each letter leading onto the other (see third line: "quitter," fifth line = "autant") her writing flows onward and forever forward, and like a river forging through a valley, she is a force to be reckoned with.

The *t*'s overcome all obstacles, the pen does not leave the paper when making the horizontal bars which, as a result of this momentum, are placed low on the stem. The heart and the spine of this writer ought to last at least a hundred years!

This woman does as she pleases, notice the *g* again—its firmness of stance. She is not a person who is easily swayed. Many of the letters have garlands in them, indicating that you can talk as much as you like, in the end she will listen only to herself.

Her overall inflexible nature can be seen in the rigid lines and the sharp angles that make up a great deal of the letter-forms. Nonetheless, there are times when this person can be relatively more flexible (see the arcades in the letter *n* in the second line "connaissance," and in the last line "donnons").

Her left margin reveals, in its increasing width, a certain degree of tiredness. This lassitude, however, is most likely not outwardly noticeable. She also exhibits a certain secrecy of nature—notice how the *s*'s are contracted and closed tight.

The *a*'s are large and overworked. This indicates the desire to love and to be loved, especially within the context of family life. This can be verified in the half-moon retrace to the left of the *a*'s (the left being toward the past as well as toward that which remains closest to the self). In this letter-form there is also a certain trace of vanity.

The *c*'s, as mentioned before, are prominent. The CAPH expresses a need to hold onto something concrete, the strength of the *c* confirms the desire to have and to possess.

This woman's mind is still alert and active. The intelligence of the ideas (QOPH = Q) is activated all the more by her imagination; again, a lunar crescent, this time in the *q* (third line: "quitter").

Her right margin has a somewhat arbitrary alignment. This authoritarian person readily turns away from the orders of others; she considers her way to be, by far, the best way.

Handwriting Sample 2

Qu'est-ce que la Suggestion ?
Il ne faut pas confondre Suggestion et persua-
sion.
Si je cherche à vous persuader, je m'adresserai
à votre raison.
J'essaierai d'obtenir votre adhésion volon-
taire et consciente.
Vous serez persuadés si vous reconnaissez
que j'ai raison, et vous donnerez votre
assentiment à mes arguments.

What is "suggestion?"

One must not confuse suggestion with persuasion.

If I try to persuade you, I will direct myself to your reason.

I will try to obtain your willing and conscious support.

You would be persuaded if you acknowledge that I am right and you would also then agree with my line of reasoning.

•   •   •

Tall and handsome, this gentleman in his 50's has a unique handwriting. He is not one to go unnoticed. The capital letters reflect his attitude toward the social setting, wherein, despite his enjoying his own originality (see the somewhat interpretive form of the capital letters) he nonetheless respects convention and good manners. Notice how he clearly indicates the beginning of a new paragraph with visual spacing and how he does not neglect to end each sentence with a period.

His line of writing fills the sheet of paper from side to side. The upper and lower loops are full. This man's self-conduct very much parallels his writing in that everything about it is large and generous. The letter *l* (first line: "la") is written clearly, fully, and is willingly connected to the following letter; from this we can deduce that the liver meridian functions well.

There is a certain hurried quality to the flow of the letters whereby they seem to jostle each other, much in the rhythm and manner of his own train of thought. The writing dances all the while remaining legible. See how it leans first to the right, then up, and then to the left. This man is in need of freedom and of space. His *h*'s have in them an open upper loop which allows us to say that the lungs relish their capacity to breathe.

The *g*'s in the first line ("suggestion") shove each other and interlock. In the second line their form is closer to that of an *f*; thus the ego, in spite of a strong and extroverted nature, is very sensitive. Much of this man's life has been hard to swallow and, similarly, he finds it equally difficult at times to put each word in its proper place.

The letter *f* in the second line shows frustration from either the mother or the spouse; one or the other is likely to have been unresponsive to his needs.

The *p*'s are prominent and somewhat despotic in imposing themselves. They hide, in fact, a weak will — as testified to by the horizontal *t* bars, in their frailty, relative to the letter's vertical stem. The heart meridian is weaker than that of the kidneys.

This man is talkative without necessarily being revealing; the *s*'s that occur at the end of his words are nearly hermetically sealed. The forcefulness of his speech can be found in the shape of his *r*'s; they are large and apparent and we can thereby assume his voice to be quite resonant (see the last line "arguments").

The z (eighth line: "reconnaissez") seems martyred or atrophied; the physical side of his sensuality has not flourished.

The overall form of the writing is without sharp angles toward the baseline and the look is basically round and well intentioned. This amiability stems from the healthy tone of the liver meridian and, again, the fullness of the l loops show this meridian to be healthy. One can see that this is not a malicious man and one from whom you could easily ask a favor.

Handwriting Sample 3

Monsieur,

J'ai l'honneur de m'adresser à vous dans le but d'obtenir votre aide quant au placement éventuel de devises étrangères.

Pourriez-vous me faire savoir quel est le taux actuel d'intérêt?

Dans l'attente de vos nouvelles, je vous prie de croire, Monsieur, à l'expression de mes sentiments distingués.

Sir,

I am pleased to address myself to you in the hopes of obtaining your assistance in eventually investing in foreign currencies. Would you let me know what is the current interest charge? While awaiting your reply, please believe, dear Sir, in my most sincere regards.

The handwriting of this 40 year old woman has notice-able *d*'s. They are disproportionately large and are retraced. The upper loop is relatively short. The *d* (DALETH) corre-sponds to the Emperor, he who is serenely seated on a golden cube, a symbol of abundance and stability. This woman's *d*'s reveal that she is in search of a solid foundation which, in her longing (the *d*'s are almost *a*'s), she imagines is part of a perfect happiness. In fact though, she is debilitating the gall bladder.

She also fears something; her *o*'s are made up of lunar crescents. To mask this fear, as well as to impose some of her own, she writes the *p*'s forcefully (next to the last line: "expression").

Like the woman in the first sample, she, too, is not someone who can easily be influenced; notice the garland shape of the *m*'s and *n*'s.

Her paragraphs are neat and precise. She is not ham-pered by disorder, evidenced all the more that this draft for a letter is written without any mistakes.

The letter *z* in "pourriez" (fourth line) is weak and diluted; she restrains herself out of fear; anxiety or fear of failure hold her back. Notice the word "interêt" in the fifth line; it reveals a great deal of her need for abundance and security.

The *i* at the beginning becomes an *e*—the male has been transformed into the female. In that same word the *n* shows her resistance to influence by others; the *t* has a loop in the stem indicating a tendency toward elaboration and bias (full-ness where none is needed). The horizontal bar of the *t* is slender and rises—perhaps with hope?

The *e* following the *t* has taken on the form of an *i*, mirroring the inversion at the beginning of the word; this time the female has been transformed into the male. At the point of going to the next letter there is a pause for reflection and then a resumption of activity into a large *r*, albeit traced with thin lines. The RESH therefore announces its decision:

the final *e* is normal and the horizontal bar of the *t* is more self assured.

Our conclusion is then that: at first she researches the matter using her feelings (*e*) and with a desire to go into action (*i*). She goes on to strengthen her determination to take action and in the process, to realize her hopes. She then pauses for reflection, and with renewed determination, from more solid ground, she goes into action.

Nonetheless, during this pause the gall bladder meridian has not contributed any of the momentum, rather it is congested and thereby hinders the liver meridian, which is itself defenseless (see the *d*'s for the gall bladder and the *o*'s for the liver). Also, the size and the loop in the *c*'s (fifth line: "actuel," seventh line: "croire") indicates some trouble with the right eye, for the weak liver discharges its ill humor into the eyes.

Handwriting Sample 4

This sample contains two different samples written several months apart, so students can see the similarities and the differences caused by time and mood.

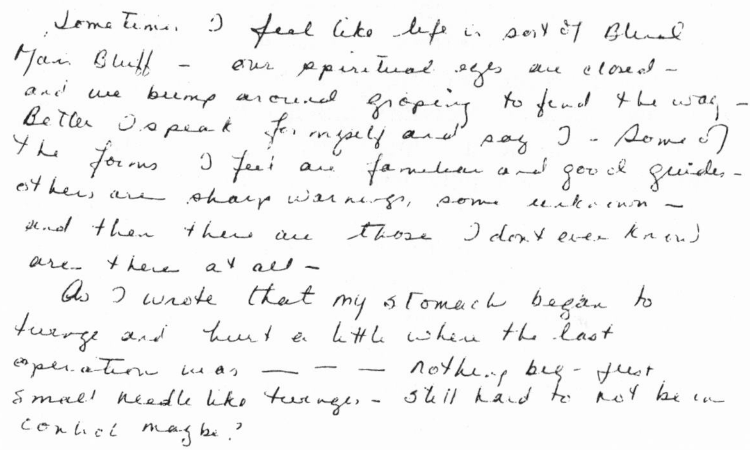
Sometimes I feel like life is sort of Blind
Man Bluff - our spiritual eyes are closed -
and we bump around groping to find the way -
Better I speak for myself and say I - Some of
the forms I feel are familiar and good guides -
others are sharp warnings, some unknown -
and then there are those I don't even know
are there at all -
As I wrote that my stomach began to
twinge and hurt a little where the last
operation was — — — nothing big - just
small needle like twinges - still hard to not be in
control maybe?

In this sample I would say that underneath a calm appearance there hides a nature with unresolved family problems, possibly a situation where there is resentment toward the upbringing in general or the mother in particular. This tension can be seen in the form of the *f*'s: they form a figure 8 in the lower loop with a rigid top bar. That this problem is chronic is indicated by the fact that, with the exception of *f* as the last letter of a word (of), all of the *f*'s are similarly formed, both in the earlier and the later sample.

Creative thrust comes from the gall bladder. Here all the *d*'s are differently and unusually formed. This meridian is not in good shape. DALETH, representing fertility or sterility, judgment, and the source of matter is here potentially creative, but for the most part remains inactive. In terms of the tarot, it is an Emperor, the 4th arcanum, who is the slave of his passions and who sits on a shaky throne.

The gall bladder meridian is also Mother of the liver and
the liver is nursed by the mother. Unfortunately for this liver,
the milk, so to speak, is irregular, it is undernourished and
sick. The *l*'s (LAMED) are small, restrained and weak. The
Hanged Man of the tarot does not wish to make the sacrifice.

In Chinese medicine the liver meridian is the sustainer of
the blood. It also forms the sexual hormones and has a decisive action upon sexual energy, including the sexual organs,
the breasts, fertility or sterility, and any other related areas.

The heart meridian is linked to that of the gall bladder;
in this case they mutually debilitate each other's balance as
the heart experiences the negative repercussions of the gall
bladder's defective state. The heart meridian also houses that
part of the sexual energy which brings life to the seminal
material. This one is in need of calm and rest. The horizontal
t bars (TAU) indicate that they are troubled from excessive
emotion. They occupy a variety of placements along or above
the vertical stem of the letter: see "Sometimes," first line,
where it is high, attached and firm; "sort of," first line, where
it is downwardly inclined; "spiritual," second line, where it is
above, detached, and concave; and more examples can be
found.

him — don't want others judgements
on it — I like the idea of travelling
in style — definitely 1st class. and he can
be fun to be with — has good taste,
intelligent, good dancer — am not so
sure about conversations — Over a period
of several hours there good — he
tends to avoid really making
any kind of personal statement.

In the second example, written by the same woman at a later date, on the second line, the word "definitely" reflects in its *d* and *t* the disorder of the gall bladder and heart meridians. The *d* here is important: it is strongly grounded into the baseline as if the Emperor were welded to his cubic throne. In this word, too, the *t* of the heart is anchored toward the ground and holds onto the following letter. These two meridians are egocentric and risk being out of control or depressed.

The loop in the letter *b* indicates that some form of anxiety has set in; the direction of the writing is from the top toward the baseline where she then forms the loop; it is toward influence from the yin—which could also predispose her toward moments of intuition. The BETHS here are those of a soul which ruminates upon thoughts that have trouble elevating themselves toward wisdom.

Many of the letterforms contain *e*'s within them. The HE represents the creation of form, inspiration, hope, the ovaries and the testicles. If this letter introduces itself in the BETH, one can reason that the anguish comes from an unrealized hope, an unmaterialized inspiration, a female sexual energy that has suffered in silence and kept its secret. However, the secret revealed itself in the form of a breast cancer. Figuratively speaking, the breast had nursed an offspring who then became the source of a deception, a deprivation, or a tragedy.

Cancer is an illness of the soul; that of this woman is unwell, nonetheless she seeks to see clearly: the word "good" in both writing samples looks like a pair of spectacles in the way that the double *o*'s are joined. This letter *o* is that of the liver in its capacity to direct visual acuity. All the while though, this woman torments and generates negativity within herself.

Overall, this person is inclined toward depression and neurosis. Her blood is malnourished, toxic, and weak. She is

unfortunately, a prime target for cancer, and did eventually
die from the disease.

Handwriting Sample 5

NOW I AM HERE FOR RESTING. THE SPRING HAS PARTLY BEEN
INTER VJUES (AND SLEEPING AFTER WARDS), PARTLY WORKING WITH
THE FACT THAT MY LIFE IS TOTALLY CHANGED. IT IS GOING TO BE
A GOOD CHANGE IN GENERAL, WHICH THE PICTURE INDICATES,
AND I KNOW SOME ABOUT IT LIKE A SILENT PLACE TO LIVE, A
SMALL LAKE TO TAKE BATHS | SWIMMING? | PADDLING CANOE? | GROWING
HERBS, AND I SUPPOSE I WILL FIND OUT MORE TO TO WITHOUT

To write all in capital letters is to deliberately hide one's
character and render it mysterious. This mystery creates an
upper hand in relation to others. This person knows how to
be amiable when she wants to be. The *h*'s are clearly formed,
the BETH represents sociability and the flow of give and
take. She is also, for the most part, clear in expressing herself
as seen in the simple and proportionate forms of the letter *p*,
PE representing speech and the expression of thoughts.

She does as she pleases: the TETH and TAU are both
firm, indicating her security in making decisions based on
full participation from both heart and mind.

The right margin is wide, though variable: she reaches
out toward others, but dislikes intrusions or authoritarian
impositions. She gives herself room enough for a retreat and
all the while sets up rigid boundaries; notice the commas, in
some cases they are nearly straight vertical lines.

The conventional forms of the letters show her to be
more cautious than one might suppose. She tests the firmness
of her ground before proceeding (note the last letter of the
words tend toward the baseline). In looking at these lines,
one has the impression that this woman makes an effort to
control and regulate the flow of her energy.

As far as men are concerned, the dots above the *i*'s (YOD) have been omitted. In general she dismisses their value for she feels herself more masculine than they. Men often seem dull to her. The brick-like facade of her writing admits little entry by others.

The *g*'s (GIMEL), the "I am" of the Empress, show how she reacts to life: some *g*'s form an *o* (spring), the AYIN of the Tower with its anxiety and its anger (originating in the liver meridian). And this anxiety comes also from the noises which she cannot assimilate. Other *g*'s are in the form of a 6, the number of VAU, 6th arcanum of the tarot, the Lovers — which is free will that stems from meditation. VAU represents here the exercise of her autonomy by way of the triple heater, which also has the correspondence of the Lovers and VAU. However, in the case of the triple heater, the free will has the potential for a personal and arbitrary aspect which this person is using to avoid hearing what displeases or threatens her.

The triple heater meridian acts upon the intensity of nervous excitation. This person, when under nervous stress, laughs in the face of danger and acts in a self-destructive, if not suicidal, manner. This disregard for her personal safety activates in her subconscious a tendency toward sexual, verbal, or possessive folly (the latter indicated in the strong *c*'s and their extended baseline stroke), which in turn causes the heat of the triple heater to rise along the back of the neck into a distribution point that then irritates the nerves in the area of the head, eyes, and ears.

She is in a tenuous position with these swings between depression and overexcitation. She needs to harmonize her consciousness and her actions if she wishes not to hear her body calling for more help. Readers should know that this is an analysis of the writing made by a woman who has been in four automobile accidents involving whiplash. All of the accidents happened while she had stopped to make a turn or wait for a light. They have created a number of physical imbalances including a condition known as TMJ, Temporo Mandibular Joint dysfunction. I did not know the extent of the injuries when I looked at this handwriting, but from the interpretation that I was able to make, it appears as though parallel to the serious outer problems there is a vast area of equally serious inner ones.

Bibliography

Casewit, Curtis. *Graphology Handbook*. West Chester, PA: Whitford Press, 1987.

Chan, Wing-tsit, tr. and comp. *A Source Book in Chinese Philosophy*. Princeton, NJ: Princeton University Press, Princeton Paperbacks, 1963.

Enel. *La Langue Sacrée*. Paris: Editions Maisonneuve-LaRose, 1984.

Fortune, Dion. *The Mystical Qabbalah*. York Beach, ME: Samuel Weiser, Inc., 1984; and Wellingborough, ENG: Thorsons Publishing Group, 1984.

Freud, Sigmund. *The Psychopathology of Everyday Life*. New York: MacMillan, 1914. (Now available New York: Norton, 1971.)

Gregory, Richard L. *Eye and Brain: The Psychology of Seeing*. New York: McGraw-Hill, 1966; and London: Weidenfeld & Nicolson, 1966.

Huard, Pierre and Ming Wong. *Chinese Medicine*. New York, Toronto: World University Library, McGraw-Hill, 1968.

Kaptchuk, Ted. *The Web That Has No Weaver: Understanding Chinese Medicine*. New York: Congdon & Weed, 1984.

Kleinman, Arthur, et al. eds. *Medicine in Chinese Cultures: Comparative Studies of Health Care in Chinese and Other Societies*. Washington, DC: John E. Fogarty International Center, U.S. Dept. of HEW, NIH, 1975.

Lao Tzu. *Tao Te Ching*. Gia-Fu Feng and Jane English, trs. New York: Random, 1972.

————. *The Way of Life*. Witter Bynner, trs. London: The Lyrebird Press, 1972.

Leslie, Charles, ed. *Asian Medical Systems*. Berkeley, CA: University of California Press, 1976.

Lin Yutang, tr. *Wisdom of Laotse*. New York: The Modern Library, 1948; and London: Greenwood Press.

Lucas, DeWitt B. *Handwriting and Character*. Philadelphia, PA: David McKay, 1923.

Nakamura, Hajime. *Ways of Thinking of Eastern Peoples*. Philip P. Weiner, ed. Honolulu: University of Hawaii, 1964.

Niboyet, *Essai sur l'Acupuncture Chinoise Pratique*. Paris: Editions Dominique Wapler, 1951.

Ogg, Oscar. *The 26 Letters*. New York: Crowell, 1961.

d'Olivet, Fabre. *The Hebraic Tongue Restored*. 1921. York Beach, ME: Samuel Weiser, Inc., 1981, 1991.

Porkert, Manfred. *The Theoretical Foundations of Chinese Medicine*. M.I.T. East Asian Science Series, Vol. 3. Cambridge, MA: M.I.T. Press, 1974.

Roman, Klara G. *Handwriting: A Key to Personality*. New York: Farrar Straus, a Noonday Press book, 1962.

Sigerist, Henry E. *A History of Medicine*, 2 vols. New York: Oxford University Press, 1961.

Solomon, Shirl. *How to Really Know Yourself Through Your Handwriting*. New York: Taplinger Publishing Co., 1985.

Soulié de Morant, George. *Chinese Acupuncture*. Brookline, MA: Paradigm Publishers, 1990.

de Surany, Marguerite. *Guide de Graphologie Moderne*. Paris: Editions de la Maisnie, 1980.

Veith, Ilza, tr. *Yellow Emperor's Classic of Internal Medicine*. Berkeley, CA: University of California Press, 1966.

Wirth, Oswald. *The Tarot of the Magicians*. York Beach, ME: Samuel Weiser, Inc., 1985.